CU00663180

Answers: P1 — P7

Section 1 — Numbers

Pages 1-2 — Ordering Numbers and Place Value

1 a) 319 ***[1 mark]***
b) Twenty thousand, six hundred and five. ***[1 mark]***
c) 5000 ***[1 mark]***

2 a) 876321 ***[1 mark]***
b) 12367 ***[1 mark]***
c) 261 ***[1 mark]***
d) One thousand, two hundred and thirty-six. ***[1 mark]***

3 a) 68, 73, 967, 985, 7432, 7480 ***[1 mark]***
b) 3.09, 3.5, 4.79, 4.8, 5.17, 5.72 ***[1 mark]***

4 a) 0.82, 0.858, 0.88, 0.904, 0.942
Elliot, Georgina, Emily, Thomas, Imogen ***[1 mark]***
b) 20.3, 20.09, 18.5, 18.1,18.06
Thomas, Imogen, Georgina, Elliot, Emily ***[1 mark]***

5 0.0064, 0.044, 0.049, 0.054, 0.578 ***[1 mark]***

Page 3 — Add, Subtract, Multiply and Divide

1 a) 5 + 15 = 20 ***[1 mark]***
5 × 4 = 20 ***[1 mark]***
5 × 2 + 10 = 20 ***[1 mark]***
b) Divide by 4 (÷4) ***[1 mark]***

2 a) −4 94 + 28 +4
= 90 + 32 ***[1 mark]***
b) ÷2 24 × 4 ×2
= 12 × 8 ***[1 mark]***

3

Calculation	✓ or ✗
(10 + 2) – 4 = 10 + 2 – 4	✓
10 + (2 × 4) = 10 + 2 × 4	✓
10 × (4 + 2) = 10 × 4 + 2	✗
(10 – 4) ÷ 2 = 10 – 4 ÷ 2	✗
(10 ÷ 2) × 4 – 2 = 10 ÷ 2 × 4 – 2	✓

[2 marks available — 2 marks for all rows correct, otherwise 1 mark for at least 3 correct rows]

Page 4 — Addition and Subtraction

1
426
+ 87
513 (carries 1 1) ***[1 mark]***

7⁷8¹2
−173
609 ***[1 mark]***

2
⁰1¹⁹0¹2 3
− 632
391 ***[1 mark]***

3 a)
5.75
+9.50
15.25 (carries 1 1) so the two tickets cost £15.25. ***[1 mark]***

b)
15.25
+6.25
21.50 (carries 1 1) so all three tickets cost £21.50. ***[1 mark]***

²3¹⁹0.¹00
−21.50
08.50 so they will get £8.50 change. ***[1 mark]***

Page 5 — Multiplying by 10,100, etc.

1 61 × 100 = 6100 ***[1 mark]***
76 × 10 = 760 ***[1 mark]***

2 a) 48 and 480 ***[1 mark]***
b) 32 and 3200 ***[1 mark]***

3 a = 0.602 × 1000 = 602
b = 6.2 × 10 = 62
c = 0.065 × 10 000 = 650
So c is the largest.
[2 marks available — 2 marks for working out the value for each number and the correct answer, otherwise 1 mark for working out at least two values correctly]

4 Bob spends:
22p × 5 = 110p
110p × 10 = 1100p = £11 ***[1 mark]***
Matt spends:
42p × 3 = 126p
126p × 10 = 1260p = £12.60 ***[1 mark]***
So Matt spends £12.60 – £11 = £1.60 more. ***[1 mark]***

Page 6 — Dividing by 10,100, etc.

1 a) 500 ÷ 10 = 50 ***[1 mark]***
b) 3400 ÷ 100 = 34 ***[1 mark]***
c) 820 000 ÷ 1000 = 820 ***[1 mark]***

2 a) 18 700 ÷ 10 = 1870 ***[1 mark]***
b) 18 700 ÷ 100 = 187 ***[1 mark]***

3 a) £1200 ÷ 6 = £200
£200 ÷ 10 = £20 ***[1 mark]***
b) The 300 pages have a thickness of:
38 mm – 1 mm – 1 mm = 36 mm. ***[1 mark]***
36 mm ÷ 3 = 12 mm
12 mm ÷ 100 = 0.12 mm ***[1 mark]***

Page 7 — Multiplying Without a Calculator

1
39
×17
27₆3
+390
663 (carry 1) ***[1 mark]***

2 a)
36
× 8
288 (carry 4) so 8 doughnuts cost 288p = £2.88 ***[1 mark]***

b)
65
×18
52₄0
+650
1170 (carry 1) so 18 cream cakes cost 1170p = £11.70 ***[1 mark]***

c)
11.70
+ 2.88
14.58 (carry 1) so the total cost is £14.58 ***[1 mark]***

¹2¹⁹0.¹⁹0¹0
−14.58
5.42 so Jenny gets £5.42 change ***[1 mark]***

Answers: P7 — P12

3 Train:

```
   67
 × 13
 2021
+ 670
  871
```

Flight:

```
   113
 ×  13
   339
+ 1130
  1469
```

So travelling by train costs £871 ***[1 mark]***
and flying costs £1469. ***[1 mark]***

```
  ⁰¹1 4̸ ¹³6 9
 −  8 7 1
    0 5 9 8
```

Flying costs £598 more. ***[1 mark]***
You could also do £113 – £67 = £46, then £46 × 13 = £598

Page 8 — Dividing Without a Calculator

1 a) 6 ⟌ 3 3 ³6 = 5 6
So 56 boxes are needed. ***[1 mark]***

b) 6 ⟌ 6 0 8 = 1 0 1 remainder 2 ***[1 mark]***
So 102 boxes are needed. ***[1 mark]***
101 full boxes and 1 box with two eggs in.

c) 55 × 9 = 495 (carry 4) so they lay 495 eggs in total. ***[1 mark]***
6 ⟌ 4 9 ¹5 = 8 2 remainder 3 ***[1 mark]***
So 83 boxes are needed. ***[1 mark]***
82 full boxes and 1 box with three eggs in.

2 a) 8 ⟌ 1 2 ⁴8 = 1 6
Lewis will have to save for 16 weeks. ***[1 mark]***

b) 5 ⟌ 2 6 ¹3 = 5 2 remainder 3 ***[1 mark]***
Andy will have to save for 53 weeks. ***[1 mark]***

c) Rick needs to save another £100 – £40 = £60. ***[1 mark]***
4 ⟌ 6 ²0 = 1 5
Rick will have to save for another 15 weeks. ***[1 mark]***

Page 9 — Negative Numbers

1 -12, -6, -5, -4, -1, 0, 7 ***[1 mark]***

2 a) Montreal ***[1 mark]***
b) 4°C – -7°C = 11°C ***[1 mark]***
c) -3°C – 12°C = -15°C ***[1 mark]***
d) 2 ***[1 mark]*** *Amsterdam and New York.*

3 a) -8 × 8 = -64 ***[1 mark]***
b) -42 ÷ -7 = 6 ***[1 mark]***
c) -9 × -8 = 72 ***[1 mark]***

Page 10 — Special Types of Number

1 a) 2p + 10p + 20p + 50p = 82p ***[1 mark]***
b) 1p + 5p = 6p ***[1 mark]***

2 a) 4, 8, 16, 38, 64 ***[1 mark]***
b) 1, 25, 49 ***[1 mark]***
c) 1, 27 ***[1 mark]***
d) 1, 64 ***[1 mark]***

3 a) $9^2 - 3^2 = 81 - 9$ ***[1 mark]***
$= 72$ ***[1 mark]***
b) $10^3 + 10^2 + 10 = 1000 + 100 + 10$ ***[1 mark]***
$= 1110$ ***[1 mark]***
c) $5^3 - 6^2 = 125 - 36$ ***[1 mark]***
$= 89$ ***[1 mark]***

Page 11 — Prime Numbers

1 a) 2 ***[1 mark]***
b) 2, 3, 5, 7, 11, 13 ***[1 mark]***
c) Only look at numbers ending in 1, 3, 7, or 9.
Then see if they divide by 3 or 7:
~~27~~ — divides by 3 so is not prime.
29 — doesn't divide by 3 or 7 so is prime.
31 — doesn't divide by 3 or 7 so is prime.
~~33~~ — divides by 3 so is not prime.
29 and 31 are the only primes between 25 and 35.
[2 marks available — 2 marks for finding the two correct prime numbers, otherwise 1 mark for finding one correct prime or if a non-prime number is included in addition to the two correct primes]

2 a) 89 ends in a 9 and doesn't divide by 3 or 7:
89 ÷ 3 = 29.666... and 89 ÷ 7 = 12.714... so 89 is a prime number.
[1 mark for saying it ends in a 9 and showing it doesn't divide by 3 or 7]
You could also show that the only factors of 89 are 1 and itself.
b) 91 ÷ 7 = 13 so 91 is not a prime number. ***[1 mark]***

3 a) 23 ***[1 mark]***
b) 73 ends in a 3 and doesn't divide by 3 or 7:
73 ÷ 3 = 24.333... and 73 ÷ 7 = 10.428... so 73 is a prime number.
[2 marks available — 1 mark for the correct answer, 1 mark for showing that it is a prime number]
You could also show that the only factors of 73 are 1 and itself.

Page 12 — Multiples and Factors

1

1	2	(3)	4	5	(6)	~~7~~	8	(9)	10
11	(12)	13	~~14~~	(15)	16	17	(18)	19	20
(~~21~~)	22	23	(24)	25	26	(27)	~~28~~	29	(30)
31	32	(33)	34	~~35~~	(36)	37	38	(39)	40

a) ***[1 mark for circles over the correct numbers]***
b) ***[1 mark for crosses over the correct numbers]***

2 a) 1, 2, 3, 4, 6, 12 ***[1 mark]***
b) 1, 2, 4, 5, 8, 10, 20, 40 ***[1 mark]***
c) 1, 2 and 4 ***[1 mark]***

3 a) Multiples of 4: 4, 8, 12, 16, 20, 24, 28, 32, 36, 40, 44, 48
Multiples of 6: 6, 12, 18, 24, 30, 36, 42, 48
The Lotto numbers that appear in both lists are 24 and 48. ***[1 mark]***
b) Multiples of 3: 3, 6, 9, 12, 15, 18, 21, 24, 27, 30, 33, 36, 39, 42, 45, 48
Factors of 54: 1, 2, 3, 6, 9, 18, 27, 54
The only Lotto number in both lists is 27. ***[1 mark]***

4 a)

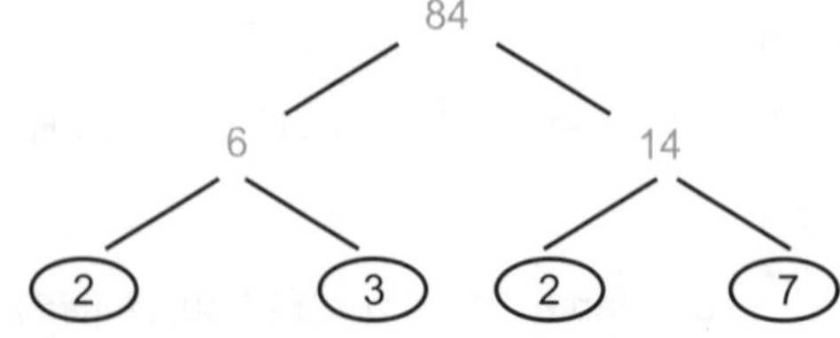

[2 marks available — 1 mark for finding the prime factors of 6, 1 mark for finding the prime factors of 14]

b) 2 × 2 × 3 × 7 (or $2^2 \times 3 \times 7$) ***[1 mark]***

Key Stage Three

Mathematics

Foundation Level

Test Practice Answer Book

Includes **Free** Online Edition

New! for the 2014 curriculum

Contents

Section 1 — Numbers 1

Section 2 — Algebra and Graphs 4

Section 3 — Ratio, Proportion and Rates of Change 6

Section 4 — Geometry and Measures 8

Section 5 — Probability and Statistics 12

Practice Paper 1 14

Practice Paper 2 16

How to get your free Online Edition

This book includes a **free** Online Edition you can read on your computer or tablet. To access it, just go to **cgpbooks.co.uk/extras** and enter this code...

4456 2380 5642 7968

By the way, this code only works for one person. If somebody else has used this book before you, they might have already claimed the Online Edition.

Published by CGP

ISBN: 978 1 78294 173 6

www.cgpbooks.co.uk

Printed by Elanders Ltd, Newcastle upon Tyne.

Clipart from Corel®

Text, design, layout and original illustrations © Coordination Group Publications Ltd. (CGP) 2014
All rights reserved.

Answers: P13 — P18

Page 13 — LCM and HCF

1 Multiples of 4: 4, 8, 12, 16, (20), 24, 28, ...
Multiples of 5: 5, 10, 15, (20), 25, 30, ...
So the LCM of 4 and 5 is 20. ***[1 mark]***

2 Factors of 42: 1, 2, 3, (6), 7, 14, 21, 42
Factors of 24: 1, 2, 3, 4, (6), 8, 12, 24
So the HCF of 24 and 42 is 6. ***[1 mark]***

3 Factors of 10: 1, (2), 5, 10
Factors of 18: 1, (2), 3, 6, 9, 18
Factors of 22: 1, (2), 11, 22
So the HCF of 10, 18 and 22 is 2.
[2 marks available — 1 mark for using the correct method, 1 mark for the correct answer]

4 Multiples of 8: 8, 16, 24, 32, (40), 48, 56, 64, 72, 80, ...
Multiples of 10: 10, 20, 30, (40), 50, 60, 70, 80, ...
So the drummers will play at the same time after 40 beats. ***[2 marks available — 1 mark for using the correct method, 1 mark for the correct answer]***

Page 14 — Fractions, Decimals and Percentages

1 a) $0.83 = \frac{83}{100}$ ***[1 mark]***
b) 8% = 0.08 ***[1 mark]***
c) $\frac{3}{5}$ = 60% ***[1 mark]***

2

Fraction	Decimal	Percentage
$\frac{3}{4}$	0.75	75%
$\frac{80}{100}$ or $\frac{8}{10}$ or $\frac{4}{5}$	0.8	80%
$\frac{51}{100}$	0.51	51%

[3 marks available — 1 mark for each fully correct row]

3 a) $43\% = \frac{43}{100}$ ***[1 mark]***
b) 3% = 0.03 ***[1 mark]***

4 a) $\frac{2}{5} = 0.4$ ***[1 mark]***
So 0.42 is greater. ***[1 mark]***
b) $\frac{3}{20} \overset{\times 5}{=} \frac{15}{100}$ = 15% ***[1 mark]***
So $\frac{3}{20}$ is greater. ***[1 mark]***

Pages 15-16 — Fractions

1 a) $\frac{12}{20} \overset{\div 4}{=} \frac{3}{5}$ ***[1 mark]***
b) $\frac{44}{100} \overset{\div 4}{=} \frac{11}{25}$ ***[1 mark]***

2 $\frac{6}{9} = \frac{2}{3}$ or $\frac{6}{2} = \frac{9}{3}$ ***[1 mark]***

3 Georgina: $\frac{5}{8} \overset{\times 3}{=} \frac{15}{24}$ Amie: $\frac{7}{12} \overset{\times 2}{=} \frac{14}{24}$
Now that the denominators are the same, you can see that Georgina has the longer toe.
[2 marks available — 1 mark for putting the fractions over the same denominator, 1 mark for the correct answer]

4 a) $4\frac{1}{5} = 4 + \frac{1}{5} = \frac{20}{5} + \frac{1}{5} = \frac{21}{5}$ ***[1 mark]***
b) 22 ÷ 9 = 2 remainder 4
So $\frac{22}{9} = 2\frac{4}{9}$ ***[1 mark]***

5 a) 195 kg ÷ 5 × 2 = 78 kg ***[1 mark]***
b) 231 miles ÷ 7 × 3 = 99 miles ***[1 mark]***

6 a) $\frac{4}{11}$ of £55 = £55 ÷ 11 × 4 = £5 × 4 = £20 ***[1 mark]***
b) $\frac{3}{5}$ of £55 = £55 ÷ 5 × 3 = £11 × 3 = £33 ***[1 mark]***
So she has £55 – £20 – £33 = £2 left ***[1 mark]***

7 a) $\frac{4}{9} + \frac{1}{6} = \frac{8}{18} + \frac{3}{18}$ ***[1 mark]*** $= \frac{11}{18}$ ***[1 mark]***
b) $\frac{4}{5} - \frac{3}{4} = \frac{16}{20} - \frac{15}{20}$ ***[1 mark]*** $= \frac{1}{20}$ ***[1 mark]***

8 a) $\frac{5}{7} \times \frac{3}{5} = \frac{15}{35} = \frac{3}{7}$ ***[1 mark]***
b) $\frac{5}{11} \div \frac{2}{3} = \frac{5}{11} \times \frac{3}{2} = \frac{15}{22}$ ***[1 mark]***

Page 17 — Percentages

1 10% of 180 = 180 ÷ 10 = 18
5% of 180 = 18 ÷ 2 = 9
15% = 10% + 5% = 18 + 9 = 27 ***[1 mark]***

2 10% of £1500 = £1500 ÷ 10 = £150
20% of £1500 = £150 × 2 = £300 ***[1 mark]***

3 66% of £88 = (66 ÷ 100) × £88 = £58.08 ***[1 mark]***

4 a) (£24 ÷ £75) × 100 = 32% ***[1 mark]***
b) 100% – 32% = 68% ***[1 mark]***

5 (£64 ÷ £40) × 100 = 160% ***[1 mark]***

Page 18 — Rounding Numbers

1

	nearest 10	nearest 100	nearest 1000
654	650	700	1000
5349	5350	5300	5000

[2 marks available — 1 mark for each correct row]

2 a) 2.4 ***[1 mark]***
b) 43.12 ***[1 mark]***

3 a) 3500 ***[1 mark]***
b) 96.5 ***[1 mark]***

4 a) 68 000 ***[1 mark]***
b) 68 390 ***[1 mark]***
c) 68 400 ***[1 mark]***

5 552 054 and 549 152 ***[1 mark]***
The answer could lie between 545 000 and 555 000 so there are two possibilities.

Answers: P19 — P25

Page 19 — Accuracy and Estimating

1 Actual value = 87
Rounded value = 90
Error = 90 – 87 = 3 ***[1 mark]***

2 Actual value = 54.846
Rounded value = 54.85
Error = 54.85 – 54.846 = 0.004 ***[1 mark]***

3 a) E.g. $51.2 \times 11 \approx 50 \times 10 = 500$ ***[1 mark]***
b) E.g. $62.9 \div 29 \approx 60 \div 30 = 2$ ***[1 mark]***
c) E.g. $\frac{301}{99 \times 2.9} \approx \frac{300}{10 \times 3} = \frac{300}{30}$ ***[1 mark]*** = 10 ***[1 mark]***

4 a) 94.8 cm × 196.4 cm ≈ 90 cm × 200 cm ***[1 mark]***
= 180 cm × 100 cm
= 18 000 cm^2 ***[1 mark]***
b) 94.8 cm × 196.4 cm ≈ 95 cm × 200 cm ***[1 mark]***
= 190 cm × 100 cm
= 19 000 cm^2 ***[1 mark]***

Page 20 — Powers

1 $1.2^3 - 0.4^2 = 1.728 - 0.16 = 1.568$ ***[1 mark]***

2 $3^4 = 81$ and $2^5 = 32$ ***[1 mark]***
$81 - 32 = 49$ ***[1 mark]***

3 a) $3^4 \times 3^5 = 3^{4+5} = 3^9$ ***[1 mark]***
b) $5^{11} \div 5^3 = 5^{11-3} = 5^8$ ***[1 mark]***

4 $2^{11} = 2^{12} \div 2$ ***[1 mark]***
$= 4096 \div 2 = 2048$ ***[1 mark]***

5 a) $\frac{2^9 \times 1^{22}}{2^7} = \frac{2^9}{2^7} = 2^{9-7}$ ***[1 mark]***
$= 2^2 = 4$ ***[1 mark]***
b) $\frac{5^{10} \div 5^8}{5^0} = \frac{5^{10-8}}{1}$ ***[1 mark]***
$= \frac{5^2}{1} = 5^2 = 25$ ***[1 mark]***

Page 21 — Square Roots and Cube Roots

1 a) 4 ***[1 mark]*** and -4 ***[1 mark]***
b) 9 ***[1 mark]*** and -9 ***[1 mark]***

2 a) 12 ***[1 mark]***
b) 4 ***[1 mark]***

3 a) $\sqrt{324} + \sqrt{441} = 18 + 21$ ***[1 mark]*** = 39 ***[1 mark]***
b) $\sqrt{484} - \sqrt{361} = 22 - 19$ ***[1 mark]*** = 3 ***[1 mark]***

4 a) $\sqrt{214}$ = 14.6287... cm = 14.6 cm (1 d.p.) ***[1 mark]***
b) $\sqrt{8654}$ = 93.0268... m = 93.0 m (1 d.p.) ***[1 mark]***

Section 2 — Algebra and Graphs

Page 22 — Algebra

1 a) $x + x + x + 2 = 3x + 2$ ***[1 mark]***
b) $3a \times a \times b = 3a^2b$ ***[1 mark]***

2 a) $5x - 6y + 3x = 5x + 3x - 6y$
$= 8x - 6y$ ***[1 mark]***
b) $7x - 4y + 2x - 1 - 3y = 7x + 2x - 4y - 3y - 1$
$= 9x - 7y - 1$ ***[1 mark]***

3 a) $6(x + 2) = 6 \times x + 6 \times 2$
$= 6x + 12$ ***[1 mark]***
b) $a(a - 1) = a \times a - a \times 1$
$= a^2 - a$ ***[1 mark]***

4 $x(2x + 3) + y(y + 1) + 3(2x + y)$
$= 2x^2 + 3x + y^2 + y + 6x + 3y$ ***[1 mark]***
$= 2x^2 + 3x + 6x + y^2 + y + 3y$
$= 2x^2 + y^2 + 9x + 4y$ ***[1 mark]***

5 a) $2(2x - 3)$ ***[1 mark]***
$= 2 \times 2x - 2 \times 3$
$= 4x - 6$ ***[1 mark]***
b) $4x - 6 + 2x - 3$ ***[1 mark]***
$= 6x - 9$ ***[1 mark]***

Page 23 — Formulas

1 $13 \times 3 + 4 = 43$ ***[1 mark]***

2 $4 \times 3 - 16 = 12 - 16$
$= -4$ ***[1 mark]***

3 $T = \frac{155 \times 4 + 400}{5}$
$T = \frac{1020}{5}$
$T = 204$ minutes
[2 marks available — 2 marks for correct answer, otherwise 1 mark for getting 1020 as the numerator]

4 $F = 45 \times 8 = 360$ ***[1 mark]***

5 $C = \frac{5(122 - 32)}{9}$
$C = \frac{5 \times 90}{9}$
$C = \frac{450}{9}$
$C = 50$
So 122 °F = 50 °C ***[1 mark]***

Page 24 — Making Formulas From Words

1 $P = \frac{N}{3} - 4$ ***[1 mark]***

2 $C = 20 + 1 \times n = 20 + n$ ***[1 mark]***

3 $Y = 4X^2 + 3$
[2 marks available — 2 marks for correct answer, otherwise 1 mark for $4X^2$]

4 £5hx ***[1 mark]***

5 $A = \frac{W - 50\,000}{3}$
[2 marks available — 2 marks for correct answer, otherwise 1 mark for W – 50 000]

Pages 25-26 — Solving Equations

1 a) $x + 6 = 9$
$x + 6 - 6 = 9 - 6$
$x = 3$ ***[1 mark]***
b) $y - 3 = 2$
$y - 3 + 3 = 2 + 3$
$y = 5$ ***[1 mark]***

2 a) $7a = 21$
$7a \div 7 = 21 \div 7$
$a = 3$ ***[1 mark]***
b) $\frac{b}{3} = 15$
$\frac{b}{3} \times 3 = 15 \times 3$
$b = 45$ ***[1 mark]***

3 a) $m + 7 = 2$
$m + 7 - 7 = 2 - 7$
$m = -5$ ***[1 mark]***

Answers: P25 — P29

b) $-\frac{n}{5} = -1$

$-\frac{n}{5} \times 5 = -1 \times 5$

$-n = -5$

$n = 5$ ***[1 mark]***

4 $19x - 7 = 6$

$19x - 7 + 7 = 6 + 7$

$19x = 13$

$19x + 3 = 13 + 3$

$19x + 3 = 16$ ***[1 mark]***

5 $3x = 5$

$3x \times 4 = 5 \times 4$

$12x = 20$ ***[1 mark]***

6 a) $2s + 1 = 5$

$2s + 1 - 1 = 5 - 1$

$2s = 4$ ***[1 mark]***

$2s \div 2 = 4 \div 2$

$s = 2$ ***[1 mark]***

b) $3r - 5 = 4$

$3r - 5 + 5 = 4 + 5$

$3r = 9$ ***[1 mark]***

$3r \div 3 = 9 \div 3$

$r = 3$ ***[1 mark]***

7 a) $2(x + 3)$

$= 2 \times x + 2 \times 3$

$= 2x + 6$ ***[1 mark]***

b) $2x + 6 = 4$

$2x + 6 - 6 = 4 - 6$

$2x = -2$ ***[1 mark]***

$2x \div 2 = -2 \div 2$

$x = -1$ ***[1 mark]***

8 $2x + 8 = 4 - 6x$

$2x + 8 - 8 = 4 - 6x - 8$

$2x = -4 - 6x$

$2x + 6x = -4 - 6x + 6x$

$8x = -4$ ***[1 mark]***

$8x \div 8 = -4 \div 8$

$x = -0.5$ ***[1 mark]***

9 a) $2x + x + 3 + 2x + x + 3 = 18$

$2x + x + 2x + x + 3 + 3 = 18$

$6x + 6 = 18$ ***[1 mark]***

b) $6x + 6 - 6 = 18 - 6$

$6x = 12$ ***[1 mark]***

$6x \div 6 = 12 \div 6$

$x = 2$ ***[1 mark]***

Pages 27-28 — Number Patterns and Sequences

1 a) 9, 15, 21 ***[1 mark]***

b) 3, 9, 27 ***[1 mark]***

2 $4 \times 2 - 3 = 5$

$5 \times 2 - 3 = 7$

$7 \times 2 - 3 = 11$

$11 \times 2 - 3 = 19$

So the next four terms are 5, 7, 11, 19.

[2 marks available — 2 marks for all correct, otherwise 1 mark for at least 2 correct]

3 To get from one term to the next you add 7. ***[1 mark]***

4 a) To move from one pattern to the next you add a row of dots. The added row contains one more dot each time.

[1 mark]

b) To get the 5th pattern you add 6 dots to the 4th pattern, so there will be 6 + 15 = 21 dots in the 5th pattern. ***[1 mark]***

5 n^{th} term: $4n - 2$

$4 \times 1 - 2 = 2$

$4 \times 2 - 2 = 6$

$4 \times 3 - 2 = 10$

[1 mark for all 3 terms correct]

6 $3 \times 15 - 5 = 40$ ***[1 mark]***

7 There are a total of $n + 2n - 1 = 3n - 1$ tiles. ***[1 mark]***

$3 \times 27 - 1 = 80$ tiles ***[1 mark]***

8 There is a difference of 2 between each term in the sequence, so $2n$ is part of the nth term.

Listing the values of $2n$, we have 2, 4, 6, 8...

To get from $2n$ to the term we must add 6, so the nth term = $2n + 6$.

[2 marks available — 2 marks for correct answer, otherwise 1 mark for getting 2n]

9 a) There is a difference of -3 between each term in the sequence, so $-3n$ is part of the nth term. ***[1 mark]***

Listing the values of $-3n$, we have -3, -6, -9, -12, -15...

To get from $-3n$ to the term we must add 7, so the nth term = $7 - 3n$.

[2 marks available — 2 marks for correct answer, otherwise 1 mark for getting -3n]

b) $7 - 3 \times 20 = -53$ ***[1 mark]***

Page 29 — X and Y Coordinates

1 a) A (1, 1) ***[1 mark]***

B (1, 5) ***[1 mark]***

C (5, 5) ***[1 mark]***

b) Point D should be drawn at (5, 1). ***[1 mark]***

c)

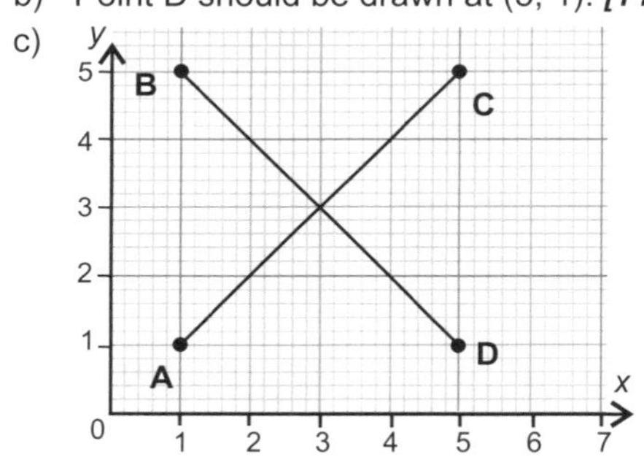

(3, 3) ***[1 mark]***

2 a)

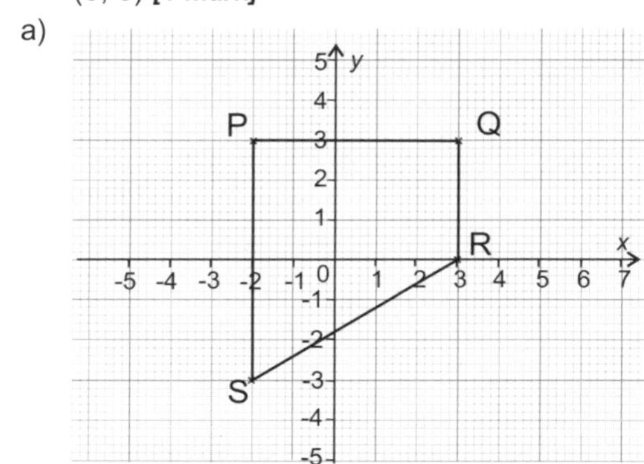

[2 marks available — 2 marks for all correct, otherwise 1 mark for 2 or 3 correct.]

b) The shape is called a trapezium. ***[1 mark]***

Answers: P30 — P34

Page 30 — Straight Line Graphs

1 a) i), ii) and iii)

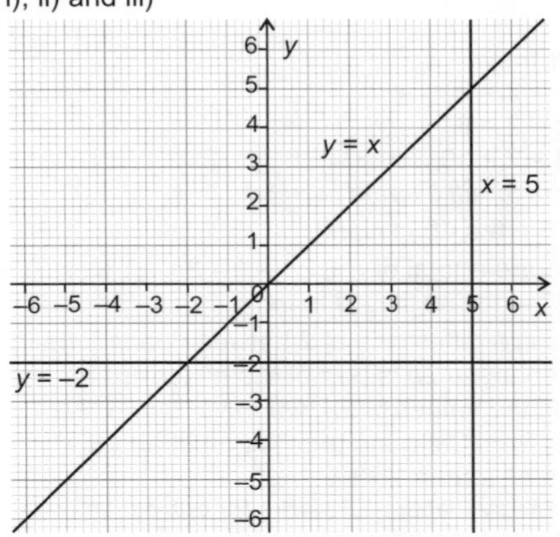

[3 marks available — 1 mark for each correct line]

b) (5, 5) *[1 mark]*

c) Right-angled or isosceles *[1 mark]*

2 a) $y = 4$ *[1 mark]*

b) $y = -1$ *[1 mark]*

c) $y = -x$ *[1 mark]*

d) (1, –1) *[1 mark]*

Page 31 — Plotting Straight Line Graphs

1 a)

x	0	3	5
y	-2	7	13

[1 mark]

b)

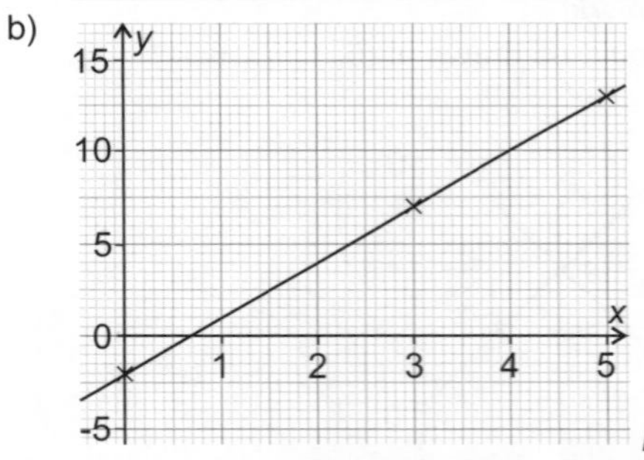

[1 mark]

c) Accept any answer with x-coordinate between 0.6 and 0.7, and y-coordinate = 0. *[1 mark]*

It actually crosses at (0.666..., 0), but you're not expected to be able to read a graph that accurately...

2 a) Only the final box should be ticked, $y = 4 - x$ *[1 mark]*

b)

x	0	2	4
y	4	2	0

[1 mark]

c)

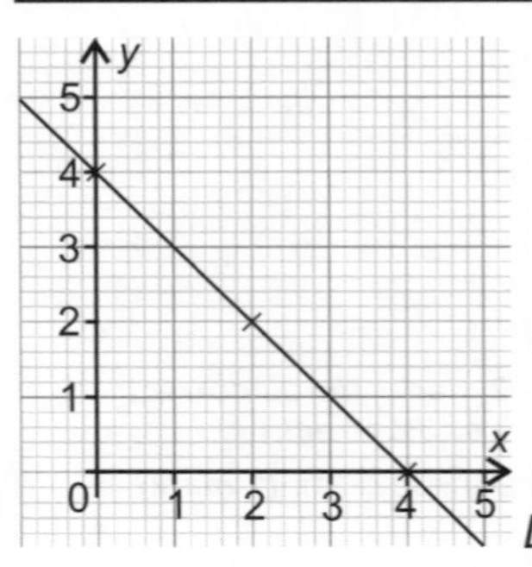

[1 mark]

Page 32 — Real-Life Graphs

1 a) \$128 *[1 mark]*

b) \$128 – \$80 = \$48 *[1 mark]*

\$48 = £30 *[1 mark]*

2 a) 15 minutes + 30 minutes = 45 minutes *[1 mark]*

b) 15 miles *[1 mark]*

When the van isn't moving the line is flat.

c) Between 12:00 and 13:00 *[1 mark]*

Section 3 — Ratio, Proportion and Rates of Change

Page 33 — Ratios

1 a) 5 : 15 (÷5)
= 1 : 3 *[1 mark]*

b) £7 : £49 (÷7)
= £1 : £7
= 1 : 7 *[1 mark]*

c) 28 cm : 8 cm (÷4)
= 7 cm : 2 cm
= 7 : 2 *[1 mark]*

2 a) 2 : 9 (×5)
= 10 : 45

So there are 10 printers in the office. *[1 mark]*

b) There are 45 computers and 3 photocopiers so the ratio of computers to photocopiers is:

45 : 3 (÷3)
= 15 : 1 *[1 mark]*

3 The total number of parts: 4 + 5 = 9
One part is: £3600 ÷ 9 = £400. *[1 mark]*
Kate gets: £400 × 4 = £1600. *[1 mark]*
Deborah gets: £400 × 5 = £2000. *[1 mark]*

4 Sam is 6 years old and Ed is 6 + 3 = 9 years old.
The ratio of their ages is 6 : 9. *[1 mark]*
The total number of parts: 6 + 9 = 15
One part is: 45 ÷ 15 = 3 sweets. *[1 mark]*
Ed gets: 3 × 9 = 27 sweets. *[1 mark]*

Pages 34-35 — Proportion Problems

1 a) £10.80 ÷ 5 = £2.16 per notebook *[1 mark]*
£2.16 × 3 = £6.48 *[1 mark]*

b) £11.25 ÷ 15 = £0.75 per pen *[1 mark]*
£0.75 × 34 = £25.50 *[1 mark]*

2 a) 40 × 4 = 160 calls in 4 hours *[1 mark]*

b) 1 call centre worker makes
40 ÷ 5 = 8 calls per hour. *[1 mark]*
8 call centre workers make
8 × 8 = 64 calls per hour. *[1 mark]*

3 a) i) 30 g ÷ 6 = 5 g in 1 sachet *[1 mark]*
20 × 5 g = 100 g in 20 sachets *[1 mark]*

ii) 6 sachets: 30 + 30 + 9 + 4 + 11 = 84 g
1 sachet: 84 g ÷ 6 = 14 g *[1 mark]*
20 sachets: 14 g × 20 = 280 g *[1 mark]*

b) 9 g ÷ 6 = 1.5 g in one sachet *[1 mark]*
15 g ÷ 1.5 g = 10 sachets *[1 mark]*

Answers: P35 — P39

4 5 sticker pack: 40 ÷ 5 = 8p per sticker
20 sticker pack: £1.20 = 120p
120 ÷ 20 = 6 = 6p per sticker
50 sticker pack: £3.50 = 350p
350 ÷ 50 = 7 = 7p per sticker
So the best value for money is the 20 sticker pack.
[3 marks available — 1 mark for finding the price per sticker for two of the packs, 1 mark for finding it for the third pack, 1 mark for the correct answer]
Alternatively you could find the amount per penny and compare.

5 A: 96 ÷ 2 = 48p per pint
B: £1.72 = 172p
172p ÷ 4 = 43p per pint
C: £2.52 = 252p
252p ÷ 6 = 42p per pint
C is the best option because you pay the least per pint.
[3 marks available — 1 mark for finding the price per pint for two of the bottles, 1 mark for finding it for the third bottle, 1 mark for the correct answer]
Alternatively you could find the amount per penny and compare.

6 a) Cheddar & Sons:
£3.60 = 360 p
400 g ÷ 360 p = 1.1111... g per penny
Cheesetastic Cheddar:
1 kg = 1000g and £9.40 = 940 p
1000 g ÷ 940 p = 1.0638... g per penny
Cheddar & Sons is better value because you get more cheese per penny.
[2 marks available — 1 mark for finding the grams per penny of the two cheeses, 1 mark for the correct answer]
Alternatively you could find the price per g or kg and compare.

b) Cheddar & Sons is better value (from part a).
6 kg = 6000 g,
6000 g ÷ 400 g = 15 packs are needed ***[1 mark]***
£3.60 × 15 = £54 ***[1 mark]***

Page 36 — Percentage Increase and Decrease

1 a) 10% of £20 = £2
£20 – £2 = £18 ***[1 mark]***

b) 10% of £18 = £1.80
£18 – £1.80 = £16.20 ***[1 mark]***

2 25% = 0.25
0.25 × 580 = 145
145 + 580 = 725 ***[1 mark]***
You could also do 1.25 × 580 = 725.

3 a) Sammie: 4% = 0.04
0.04 × £320 = £12.80
Joe: 3% = 0.03
0.03 × £420 = £12.60
So Sammie gets more interest each year.
[2 marks available — 2 marks for working out each amount of interest correctly and giving the correct answer, otherwise 1 mark for working out one amount of interest correctly]

b) Interest in 5 years: £12.60 × 5 = £63 ***[1 mark]***
Total after 5 years: £420 + £63 = £483 ***[1 mark]***

Page 37 — Conversion Factors

1 a) 1 kg = 1000 g so the conversion factor is 1000.
374 ÷ 1000 = 0.347 kg ***[1 mark]***
If you're not sure what to do in a conversion question, multiply and divide by the conversion factor, then pick the sensible answer.

b) 1 cm = 10 mm so the conversion factor is 10.
20.2 × 10 = 202 mm ***[1 mark]***

2 a) 1 yard = 3 feet so the conversion factor is 3.
22 yards = 22 × 3 = 66 feet ***[1 mark]***

b) 1 foot = 12 inches so the conversion factor is 12.
66 feet = 66 × 12 = 792 inches ***[1 mark]***

3 a) 1 kg ≈ 2.2 lb so the conversion factor is 2.2.
33 ÷ 2.2 = 15 so 33 lb ≈ 15 kg ***[1 mark]***

b) Total weight loss will be 44 + 33 = 77 lb. ***[1 mark]***
1 stone = 14 lb so the conversion factor is 14.
77 lb ÷ 14 = 5.5 stones ***[1 mark]***

4 Tank A:
1 gallon ≈ 4.5 litres so the conversion factor is 4.5.
12 × 4.5 = 54 so 12 gallons ≈ 54 litres
Tank B: 56 litres
Tank C:
1 cm^3 = 1 ml so 52000 cm^3 = 52000 ml
1 litre = 1000 ml so the conversion factor is 1000.
52000 ml ÷ 1000 = 52 litres
So tank B is the biggest.
[2 marks available — 2 marks for converting all sizes to the same units and giving the correct answer, otherwise 1 mark for converting one of the sizes correctly]

Page 38 — Time and Timetables

1 a) Departure time: 15 – 12 = 3 so 15:20 = 3:20 pm ***[1 mark]***
Arrival time: 19 – 12 = 7 so 19:05 = 7:05 pm ***[1 mark]***

b) 3:20 pm + 3 hours = 6:20 pm
6:20 pm + 40 minutes = 7:00 pm
7:00 pm + 5 minutes = 7:05 pm
The coach journey was 3 hours and 45 minutes ***[1 mark]***

2 a) 1 hour = 60 minutes
1 hour and 50 minutes = 60 + 50
= 110 minutes ***[1 mark]***

b) 7:30 pm + 1 hour = 8:30 pm
8:30 pm + 50 minutes = 9:20 pm ***[1 mark]***
9 + 12 = 21 so 9:20 pm = 21:20 ***[1 mark]***

3 a) 13 – 12 = 1 so 13:16 = 1:16 pm ***[1 mark]***

b) 1 + 12 = 13 so 1:20 pm = 13:20
The next bus from Market Square is at 13:33 so you will have to wait 33 – 20 = 13 minutes ***[1 mark]***

c) 2 + 12 = 14 so 2:00 pm = 14:00
The last bus to arrive at the bus station before 14:00 is at 13:47. This bus leaves English Street at 13:28.
13 – 12 = 1 so 13:28 = 1:28 pm ***[1 mark]***

Page 39 — Maps and Scale Drawings

1 a) The map distance from the Banyan Tree to the Castle is 5 cm. ***[1 mark]***
Real-life distance = 5 × 4 = 20 km ***[1 mark]***

b) The map distance from the Misty Mountain to the Hidden Caves is 2.7 cm. ***[1 mark]***
Real-life distance = 2.7 × 4 = 10.8 km ***[1 mark]***

Answers: P39 — P44

c) The treasure is 12 ÷ 4 = 3 cm west of the Waterfall.

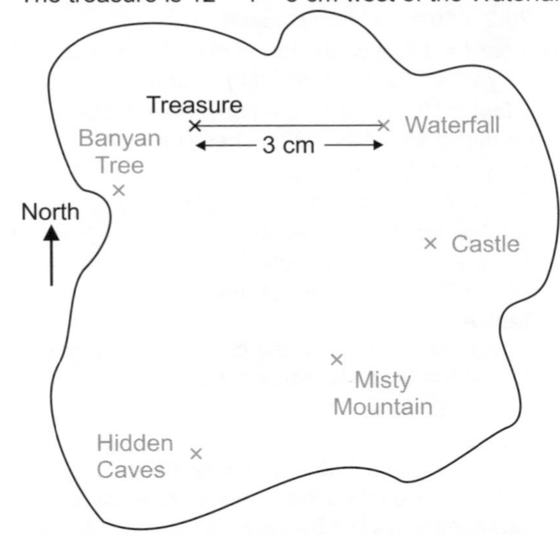

[2 marks available — 1 mark for finding that the treasure is 3 cm west of the Waterfall, 1 mark for marking the position of the treasure correctly]

2 The length of the longest side of the rug on the scale drawing is 5 cm. *[1 mark]*
Real-life length of the rug:
5 × 100 = 500 cm = 5 m *[1 mark]*

3 a) Real-life length: 9 × 50 = 450 cm *[1 mark]*
b) Length of model: 11 ÷ 50 = 0.22 m *[1 mark]*
= 22 cm *[1 mark]*

Page 40 — Speed

1 a) 12 km ÷ 3 hours = 4 km/h *[1 mark]*
b) 20 m ÷ 40 seconds = 0.5 m/s *[1 mark]*

2 From 8 am to 11 am there are 11 – 8 = 3 hours. *[1 mark]*
50 km/h × 3 hours = 150 km *[1 mark]*

3 a) 9.6 km/h × 3 hours = 28.8 km *[1 mark]*
b) 10.8 km/h × 3 hours = 32.4 km *[1 mark]*
32.4 km – 28.8 km = 3.6 km *[1 mark]*

4 It took Ben 180 ÷ 40 = 4.5 hours to get from his house to the airport. *[1 mark]*
4.5 hours = 4 hours and 30 minutes
He left at 11 am, so he got to the airport at:
11 am + 4 hours + 30 minutes
= 3 pm + 30 minutes
= 3:30 pm or 15:30 *[1 mark]*

Section 4 — Geometry and Measures

Page 41 — Symmetry

1 a) O *[1 mark]*
b) O, S *[1 mark]*
c) E *[1 mark]*

2 a)

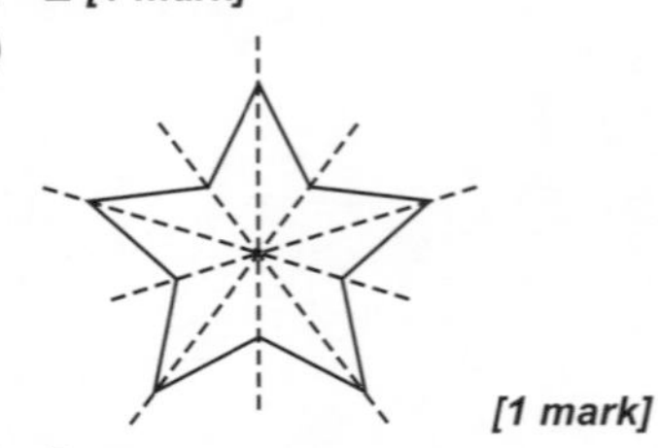

[1 mark]

b) 5 *[1 mark]*

3

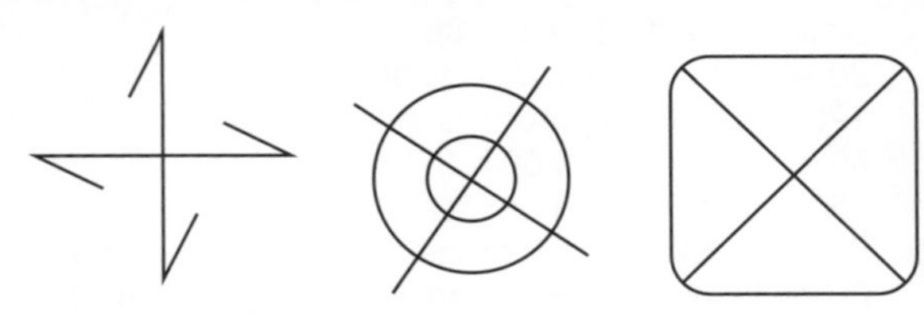

[3 marks available — 1 mark for each correct diagram]

Page 42 — 2D Shapes

1

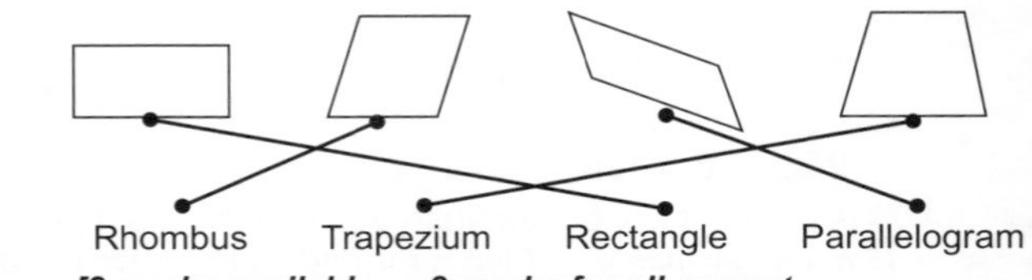

[2 marks available — 2 marks for all correct, otherwise 1 mark for 2 correct]

2 a) 2, 1, 1
[3 marks available — 1 mark for each correct answer]
b) 2, 1
[2 marks available — 1 mark for each correct answer]

3

Type of Triangle	Equilateral triangle	Isosceles triangle	Scalene triangle
Diagram			
Number of equal angles	3	2	0

[3 marks available — 1 mark for each correct column]

4 90°, 45° and 45°
[2 marks available — 1 mark for 90° and 1 mark for 45° and 45°]
It has one line of symmetry, so it must have 2 equal angles.

Page 43 — Regular Polygons

1 Square, Equilateral triangle *[1 mark]*

2 a)

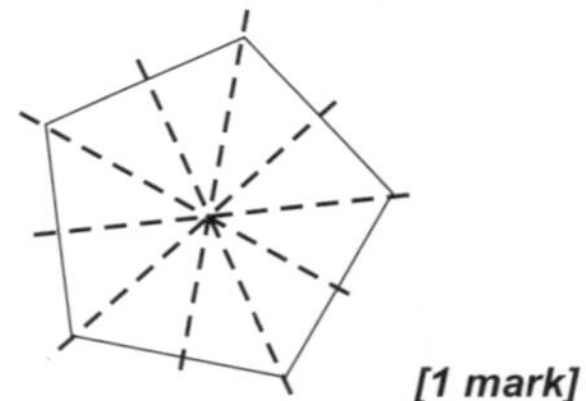

[1 mark]

b) 5 *[1 mark]*

3 a) Heptagon *[1 mark]*
b) 7 *[1 mark]*
c) 7 *[1 mark]*

Page 44 — Congruence and Similarity

1 C, E
[2 marks available — 2 marks for correct answer, otherwise 1 mark for 1 correct letter, or if any letter is given in addition to the correct answer]

2 3 *[1 mark]*

Answers: P45 — P50

Page 45 — Perimeter

1 a) 30 + 20 + 30 + 20 = 100 cm ***[1 mark]***

b) 20 cm ÷ 2 = 10 cm ***[1 mark]***
30 + 10 + 30 + 10 = 80 cm ***[1 mark]***

2 24 – 10 = 14 cm
14 ÷ 2 = 7 cm
The sides are 7 cm and 7 cm.
[2 marks available — 2 marks for correct answer, otherwise 1 mark for 24 – 10 = 14 cm]
The marks on the sides of the triangle show you that the two sides have equal lengths.

3 a)

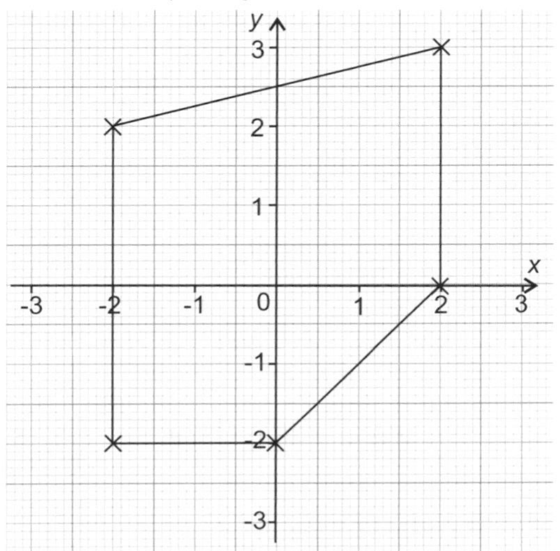

[2 marks available — 2 marks for all points correct and joined together, otherwise 1 mark for at least 3 points correct]

b) Perimeter = 20 + 40 + 41 + 30 + 28 = 159 mm
[2 marks available — 1 mark for all measurements correct within one mm, 1 mark for correctly adding up measurements]

Pages 46-47 — Area

1 Area = base × height = 2.5 × 4 = 10 cm² ***[1 mark]***

2 a) Add the lengths of the parallel sides, multiply by the distance between them and then divide by 2.
The formula is $\frac{1}{2}(a+b) \times \text{height}$.
[1 mark for correct explanation or formula]

b) $\frac{1}{2}(a+b) \times \text{height} = \frac{1}{2}(4+5) \times 3$
= 13.5 cm²
[2 marks available — 2 marks for correct answer, otherwise 1 mark for correct substitution into formula]

3 21 ÷ 6 = 3.5 cm ***[1 mark]***

4 Area = $\frac{1}{2}(\text{base} \times \text{height})$
= $\frac{1}{2}(21 \times 24)$ = 252 cm²
[2 marks available — 2 marks for correct answer, otherwise 1 mark for correct substitution into formula]
When you're finding the area of a triangle, all you need is the length of the base and the vertical height.

5 Area of rectangular section = 4.5 × 2 = 9 m²
Area of triangular section = (2 × 1.5) ÷ 2 = 1.5 m²
Total area = 9 + 1.5 = 10.5 m²
[2 marks available — 2 marks for correct answer, otherwise 1 mark for correctly finding area of rectangle or triangle]

6 Split the T shape into two rectangles:
Area of horizontal rectangle = 20 × 3 = 60 cm²
Area of vertical rectangle = (20 – 7 – 7) × 16 = 6 × 16
= 96 cm²
Area of T shape = 60 + 96 = 156 cm²
[3 marks available — 3 marks for correct answer, otherwise 1 mark for splitting the shape into smaller rectangles and 1 mark for correctly finding their areas]
You could also split the shape into three rectangles — two 3 cm × 7 cm rectangles either side of a 19 cm × 6 cm rectangle.

7 Area of rectangle = 9.2 × 4.5 = 41.4 cm² ***[1 mark]***
Area of rhombus = [(8 × 3) ÷ 2] × 4
= 12 × 4
= 48 cm² ***[1 mark]***
So, the rhombus has the larger area. ***[1 mark]***
To find the area of a complicated shape, break it down into easier shapes like rectangles and triangles.

Page 48 — Circles

1 Radius = 80 ÷ 2 = 40 cm
Area = π × 40² = 5026.54824... cm² ***[1 mark]***
= 5026.55 cm² (2 d.p.) ***[1 mark]***

2 Diameter = 1.6 × 2 = 3.2 m
Circumference = 3.2 × π = 10.05309... m ***[1 mark]***
= 10.05 m (2 d.p.) ***[1 mark]***

3 Area of circle = 3² × π = 28.27433... cm² ***[1 mark]***
Area of the rectangle = 25 × 8 = 200 cm² ***[1 mark]***
Area of remaining metal:
200 – 28.27433... = 171.72566... cm²
= 171.73 cm² ***[1 mark]***

Page 49 — 3D Shapes

1 a) tetrahedron ***[1 mark]***
b) cuboid ***[1 mark]***
c) sphere ***[1 mark]***

2 a) triangular prism ***[1 mark]***
b) cylinder (or circular prism) ***[1 mark]***
c) square-based pyramid ***[1 mark]***

3 a) 5 ***[1 mark]***
b) 8 ***[1 mark]***
c) 9 ***[1 mark]***

Pages 50-51 — Nets and Surface Area

1 B and D should be ticked.
[2 marks available — 2 marks for correct answer, otherwise 1 mark for 1 correct or if one additional box is ticked]

2 Triangular prism, tetrahedron
[2 marks available — 1 mark for each correct answer]

3

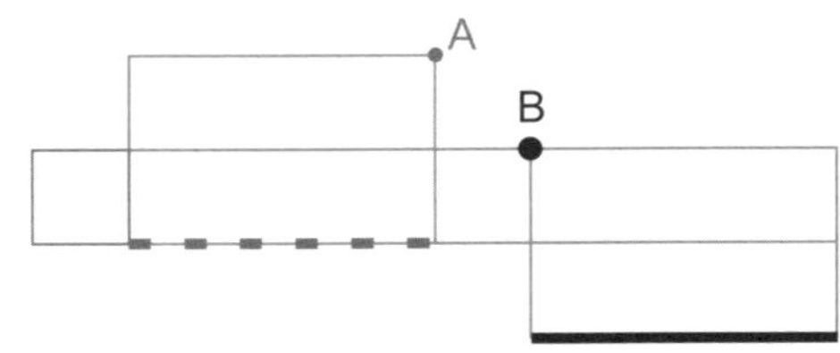

[2 marks available — 1 mark for correct point B, 1 mark for correct bold line]

Answers: P51 — P57

4 a) E.g.

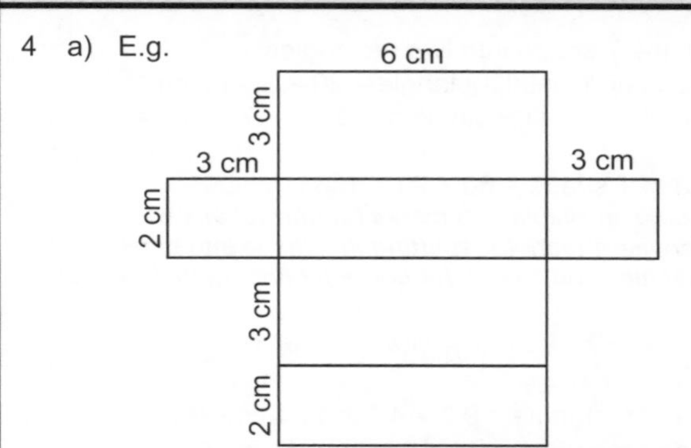

[2 marks available — 1 mark for correct net, 1 mark for correct labels]

b) Area of base = $6 \times 2 = 12$ cm^2
Area of front = $6 \times 3 = 18$ cm^2
Area of side = $3 \times 2 = 6$ cm^2
Surface area of cuboid = $2 \times 12 + 2 \times 18 + 2 \times 6$
= 72 cm^2
[2 marks available — 2 marks for correct answer, otherwise 1 mark for correct separate areas, allowing for one numerical error]

5 a) E.g.

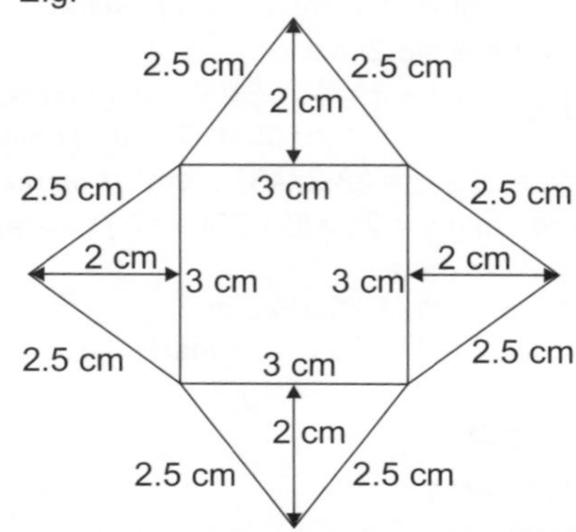

[2 marks available — 1 mark for drawing the correct net, 1 mark for labelling it correctly]

b) Area of square = $3 \times 3 = 9$ cm^2
Area of each triangle = $\frac{1}{2} \times 2 \times 3 = 3$ cm^2
Surface area = $9 + (4 \times 3) = 21$ cm^2
[2 marks available — 2 marks for correct answer, otherwise 1 mark for correctly working out separate areas, allowing for one numerical error]

Page 52 — Volume

1 $2.4 \times 0.8 \times 0.5 = 0.96$ m^3 ***[1 mark]***

2 a) $0.5 \times 11 \times 8 = 44$ cm^2 ***[1 mark]***
The cross section is a triangle.
b) $44 \times 10 = 440$ cm^3 ***[1 mark]***

3 a) Cross-section = $\pi \times 3.7^2 = 43.00840...$ cm^2
= 43.01 cm^2 (2 d.p.) ***[1 mark]***
b) $43.00840... \times 11 = 473.09243...$ cm^3
= 473.09 cm^3 (2 d.p.) ***[1 mark]***

Page 53 — Lines and Angles

1 DAB = 90° ***[1 mark]***
BCD = 45° ***[1 mark]***

2 a) i) obtuse ***[1 mark]***
ii) acute ***[1 mark]***
b) i) 152° (accept 151° or 153°) ***[1 mark]***
ii) 29° (accept 28° or 30°) ***[1 mark]***

3 a) 35° ***[1 mark]***
b) 145° ***[1 mark]***

Pages 54-55 — Angle Rules

1 $a = 180° - (35° + 40°) = 180° - 75° = 105°$ ***[1 mark]***
The sum of the angles in a triangle is 180°.
$b = 180° - (30° + 42° + 67°) = 180° - 139° = 41°$ ***[1 mark]***
Angles on a straight line add up to 180°.

2 $c = 360° - (104° + 90°) = 360° - 194° = 166°$ ***[1 mark]***
Angles around a point add up to 360°.
$d = 360° - (82° + 87° + 103°)$
$= 360° - 272° = 88°$ ***[1 mark]***
The sum of angles in a quadrilateral is 360°.

3 $180° - 40° = 140°$ ***[1 mark]***
$a = 140 \div 2 = 70°$ ***[1 mark]***
The triangle is isosceles, so it has two equal angles.

4 The triangle is isosceles, so $b = 35°$ ***[1 mark]***
$c = 180° - (35° + 35°) = 110°$ ***[1 mark]***

5 Third angle in triangle = $180° - 31° - 69° = 80°$ ***[1 mark]***
So using angles on a straight line, $d = 180° - 80°$
$= 100°$ ***[1 mark]***

Page 56 — Parallel Lines

1 a is vertically opposite 47°, so $a = 47°$.
b is vertically opposite 133°, so $b = 133°$.
[2 marks available — 1 mark for each correct answer]

2 c is vertically opposite 73°, so $c = 73°$.
c and d are corresponding angles, so $d = 73°$.
e and d are angles on a straight line, so
$e = 180° - 73° = 107°$.
[3 marks available — 1 mark for each correct answer]

3 f and 110° are angles on a straight line, so
$f = 180° - 110° = 70°$.
g and the 110° angle are alternate angles, so $g = 110°$.
[2 marks available — 1 mark for each correct answer]

4 h and the 80° angle are corresponding angles,
so $h = 80°$.
i is vertically opposite h, so $i = 80°$.
j and the 72° angle are alternate angles, so $j = 72°$.
[3 marks available — 1 mark for each correct answer]

Page 57 — Interior and Exterior Angles

1 a) $360 \div 7 = 51.42857...° = 51.4°$ ***[1 mark]***
b) $180° - 51.42857...° = 128.57142...° = 128.6°$ ***[1 mark]***
c) $128.57142... \times 7 = 900°$ ***[1 mark]***
Alternatively, use the formula for the sum of interior angles.
$(n - 2) \times 180° = (7 - 2) \times 180° = 900°$.

2 $(n - 2) \times 180° = (20 - 2) \times 180° = 18 \times 180° = 3240°$
[2 marks available — 1 mark for using the correct formula, 1 mark for the correct answer]

3 Sum of the interior angles of a hexagon:
$(n - 2) \times 180° = (6 - 2) \times 180°$ ***[1 mark]***
$= 4 \times 180° = 720°$ ***[1 mark]***
$x = 720° - 110° - 95° - 130° - 143° - 30°$
$= 212°$ ***[1 mark]***

Answers: P58 — P61

Page 58 — Translations

1 a) $\begin{pmatrix} -3 \\ -4 \end{pmatrix}$ ***[1 mark]***

b) $\begin{pmatrix} 5 \\ 1 \end{pmatrix}$ ***[1 mark]***

2

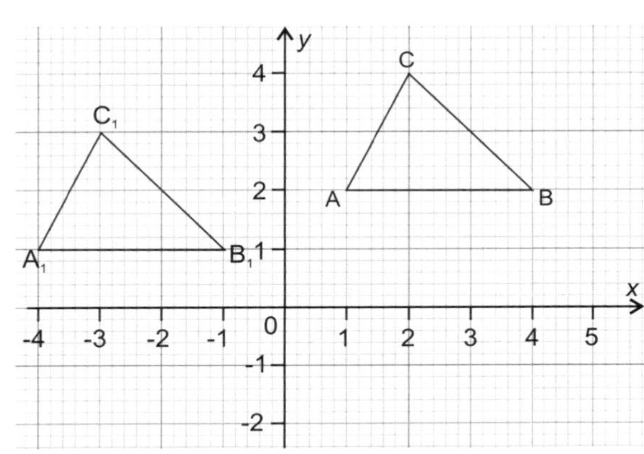

[2 marks available — 1 mark for correct shift in x-direction and 1 mark for correct shift in y-direction]

Page 59 — Reflections

1

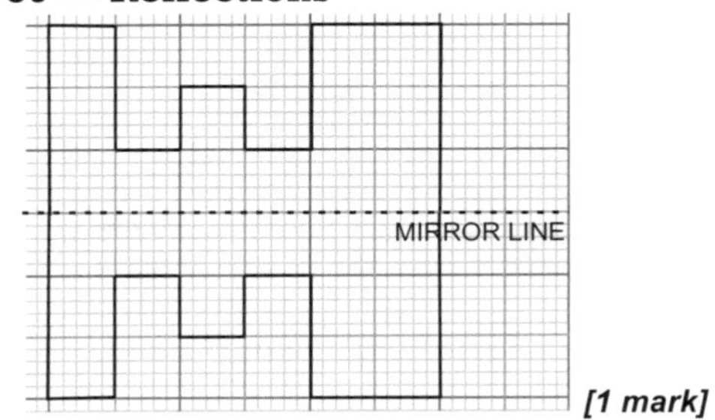

[1 mark]

2

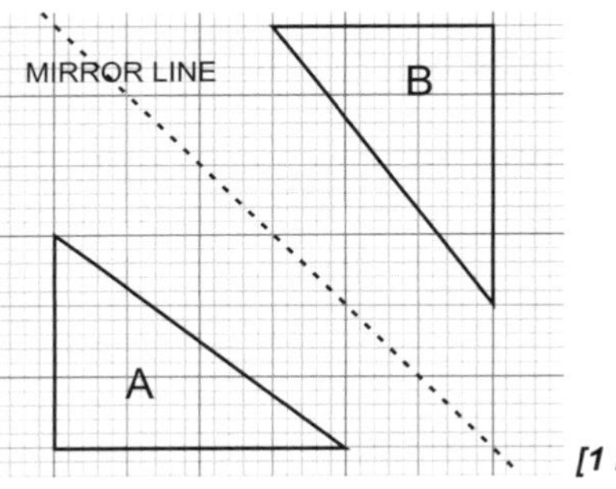

[1 mark]

3

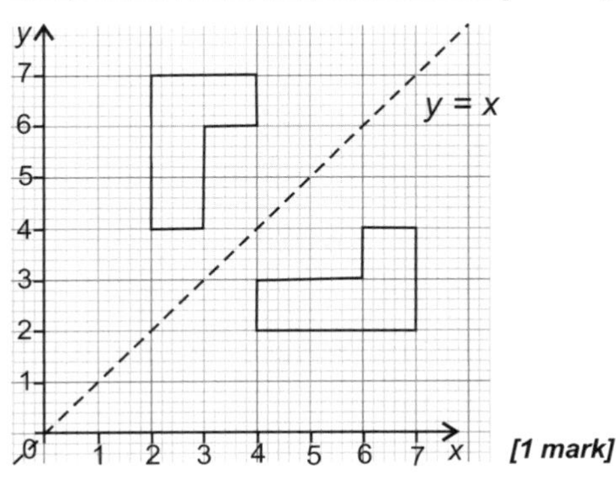

[1 mark]

Page 60 — Rotations

1

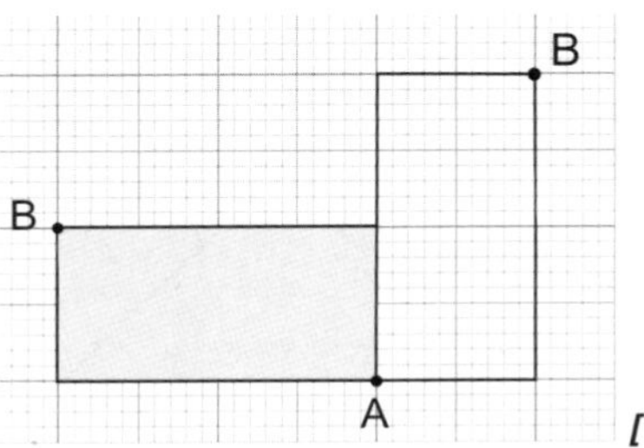

[1 mark]

2 a)

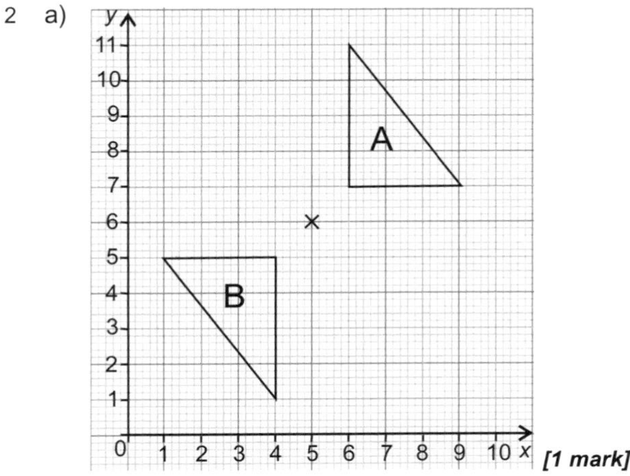

[1 mark]

b) 180° ***[1 mark]***

3

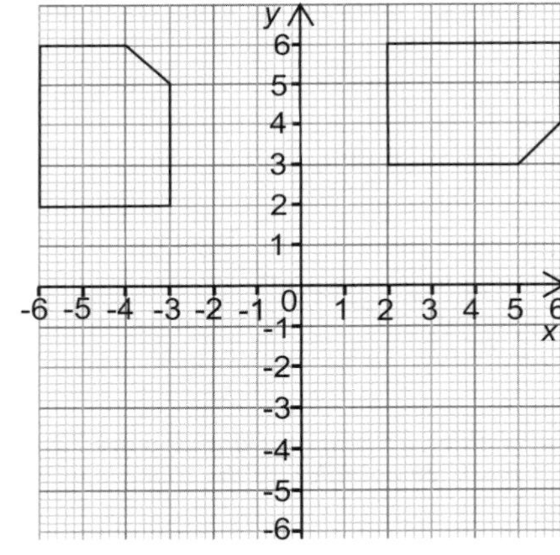

[2 marks available — 1 mark for shape rotated 90° anticlockwise, 1 mark for correct position on grid]

Page 61 — Enlargements

1

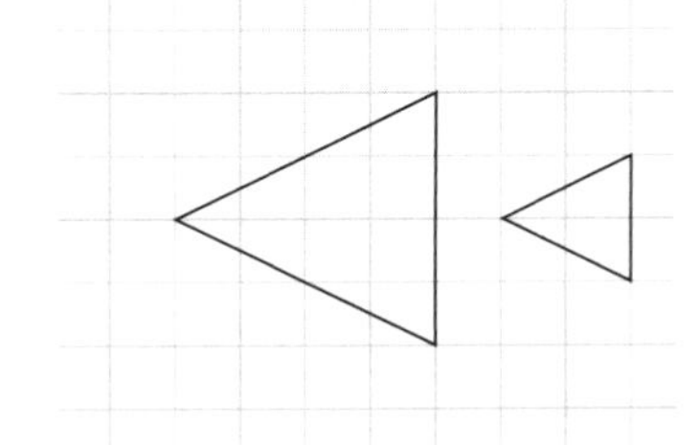

[1 mark for shape of correct size]

2 a) i) 4 ÷ 2 = 2 ***[1 mark]***

Divide a side length on B by the corresponding side length on A.

ii) (5, 1) ***[1 mark]***

Draw lines through corresponding vertices of shapes A and B. The lines cross at the centre of enlargement.

Answers: P61 — P65

b)

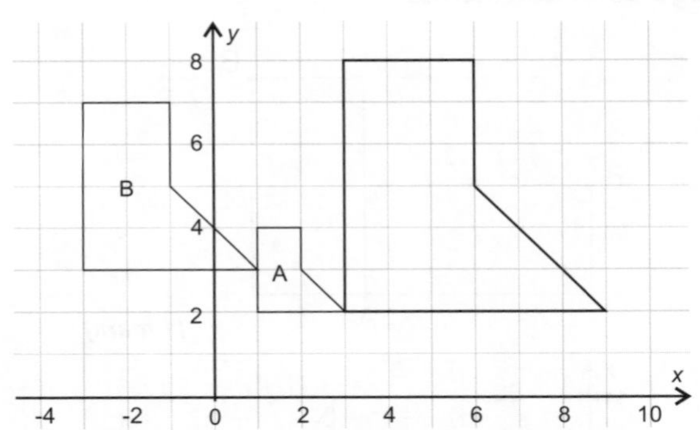

[2 marks available — 1 mark for shape of correct size, 1 mark for the correct position]

Pages 62-63 — Constructions

1

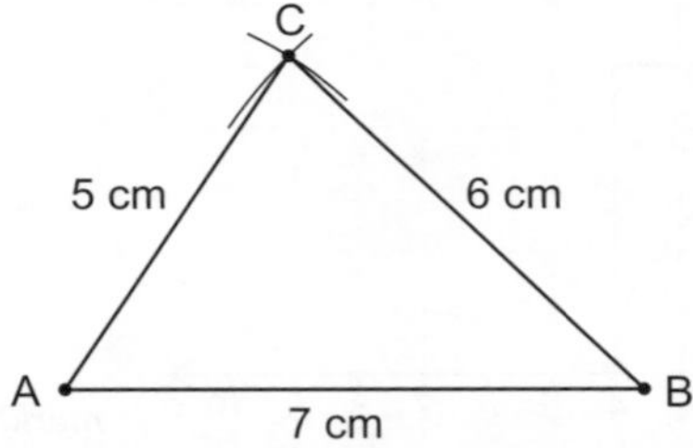

[2 marks available — 1 mark for correctly drawn construction arcs, 1 mark for a correct and accurate triangle]

2

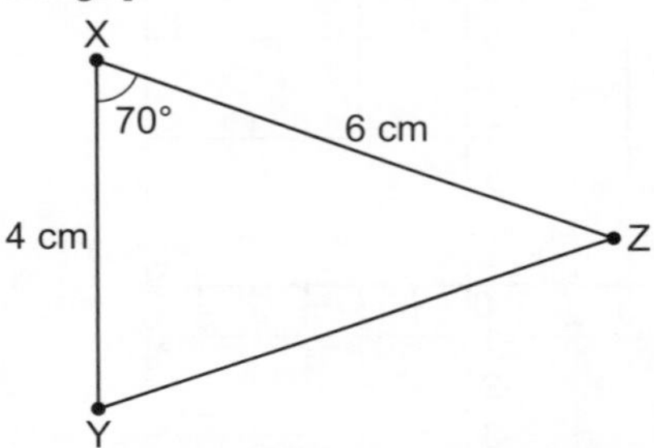

[2 marks available — 1 mark for drawing the 70° angle correctly, 1 mark for completing the triangle with XZ = 6 cm]

3

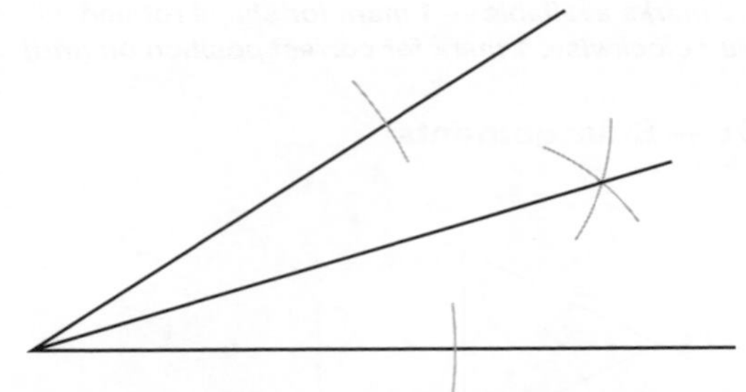

[2 marks available — 1 mark for correctly drawn construction arcs, 1 mark for an accurate bisection that divides the angle exactly in half]

4

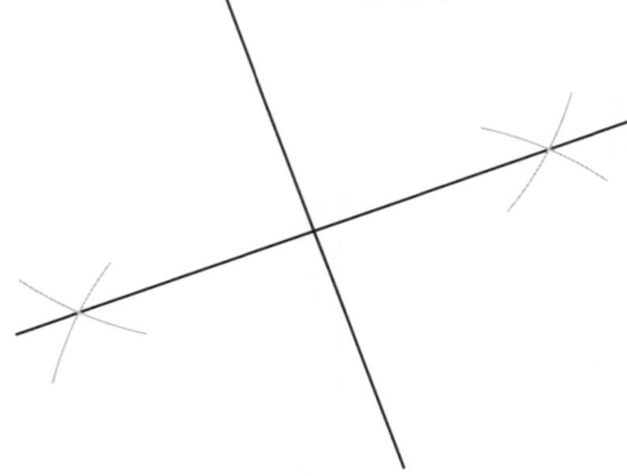

[2 marks available — 1 mark for correctly drawn construction arcs, 1 mark for an accurate bisection that divides the line exactly in two and intersects the line at right angles]

5

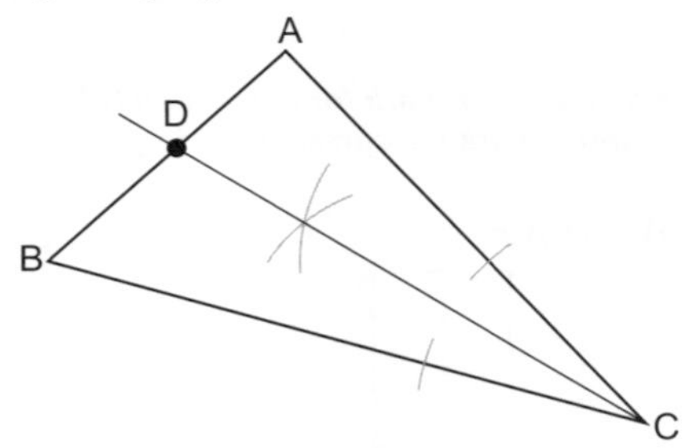

a) ***[2 marks available — 1 mark for correctly drawn construction arcs, 1 mark for an accurate bisection of angle ACB]***

b) 26 mm (accept 25 mm or 27 mm) ***[1 mark]***

Section 5 — Probability and Statistics

Pages 64-65 — Probability

1 a) 0.3 ***[1 mark]***

b) Mark ***[1 mark]***

c) Bill ***[1 mark]***

2 a) $\frac{4}{9}$ ***[1 mark]***

b) $\frac{3}{9}$ or $\frac{1}{3}$ ***[1 mark]***

c) $\frac{6}{9}$ or $\frac{2}{3}$ ***[1 mark]***

3 $1 - \frac{1}{5} = \frac{4}{5}$ or 0.8 ***[1 mark]***

4 a) $\frac{3}{8}$ ***[1 mark]***

b) P(landing on shaded) $= 1 - \frac{2}{3} = \frac{1}{3} = \frac{2}{6}$

So 2 of the 6 sections should be shaded, e.g.

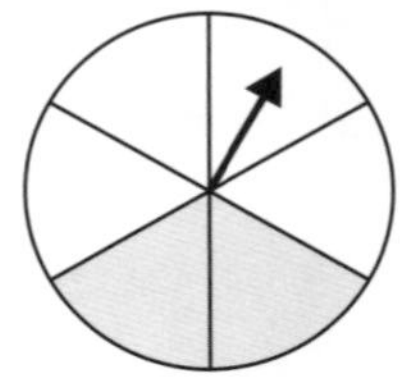

Spinner B ***[1 mark]***

Answers: P65 — P69

5 a)

	1	2	3	4	5	6
Head (H)	H1	H2	H3	H4	H5	H6
Tail (T)	T1	T2	T3	T4	T5	T6

[1 mark]

b) $\frac{1}{12}$ *[1 mark]*

c) $\frac{3}{12}$ or $\frac{1}{4}$ *[1 mark]*

6 a) P(Lemon) = $\frac{6}{20}$ or $\frac{3}{10}$ or 0.3 *[1 mark]*

b) P(Lemon) = $\frac{6}{20}$, P(Strawberry) = $\frac{2}{5}$

So P(Lime) = $1 - \frac{6}{20} - \frac{2}{5}$ *[1 mark]*

$= \frac{20}{20} - \frac{6}{20} - \frac{8}{20} = \frac{6}{20}$ or $\frac{3}{10}$ or 0.3 *[1 mark]*

Page 66 — Venn Diagrams

1 a) 6, 8, 10, 16 *[1 mark]*

b) 8, 10 *[1 mark]*

c) 6 *[1 mark]*

2

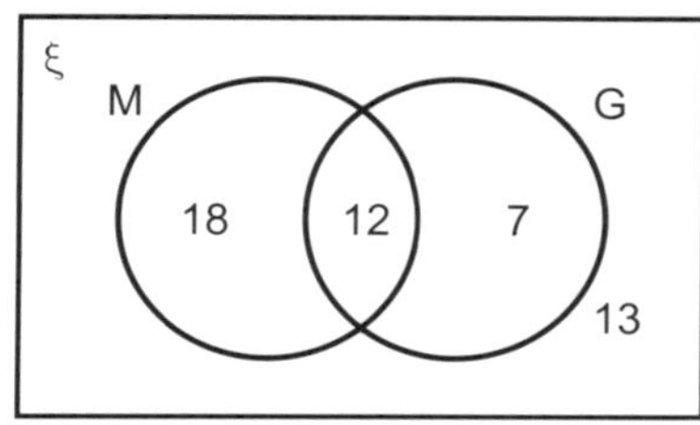

[2 marks available — 2 marks for diagram fully correct, otherwise 1 mark for 2 labels correct]

3 a) ξ = {1, 2, 3, 4, 5, 6, 7, 8, 9, 10, 11, 12, 13, 14, 15},
P = {1, 3, 5, 7, 9, 11, 13, 15} and Q = {3, 6, 9, 12, 15},
P and Q = {3, 9, 15}

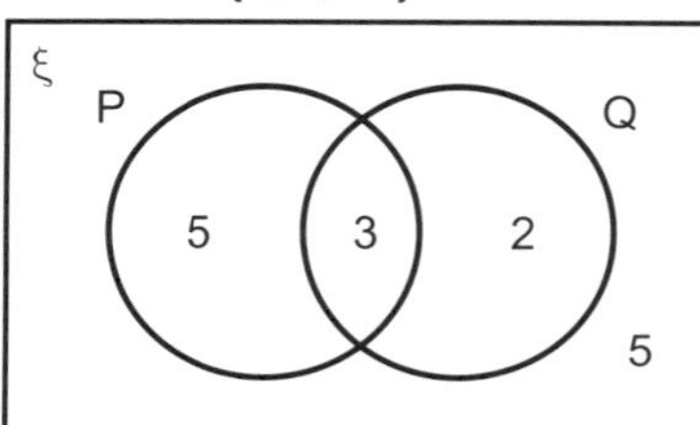

[3 marks available — 3 marks for completely correct diagram, otherwise award 1 mark for 2 numbers correct or 2 marks for 3 numbers correct]

b) 2 + 5 = 7 *[1 mark]*

Page 67 — Line Graphs and Pictograms

1 a) 3.5 × 4 = 14 *[1 mark]*

b) 16 ÷ 4 = 4 footballs need to be drawn.

[1 mark]

c) (3.5 + 2 + 3 + 1 + 4) × 4 = 54 *[1 mark]*

2 a)

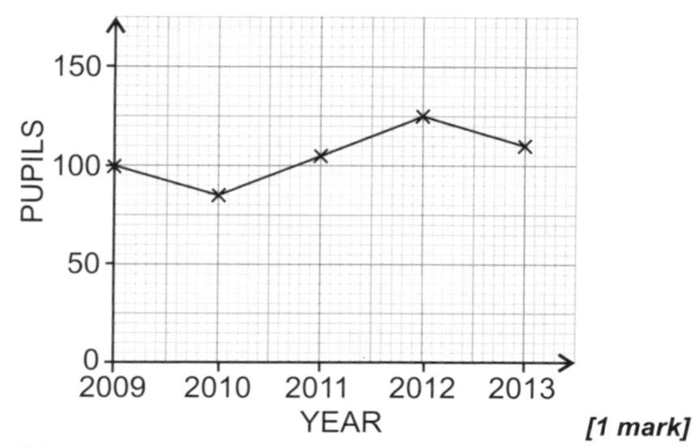

[1 mark]

b) 2012 *[1 mark]*

c) You would need to know how many Year 11 pupils there were in total in 2010. If there were only 85 pupils in 2010 then the school did well to keep them all.
[1 mark]

Page 68 — Bar Charts

1 a) Tennis *[1 mark]*

b) 21 + 12 = 33 *[1 mark]*

c) 24 – 12 = 12 *[1 mark]*

2 a) 15 *[1 mark]*

b) 24 + 17 = 41 *[1 mark]*

c) 2 *[1 mark]* *It is the highest Year 7 bar.*

d) 23 – 15 = 8 *[1 mark]*

Page 69 — Pie Charts

1 a) Lee *[1 mark]*
Out of the 3 friends he has the largest angle for "reading".

b) Jeff *[1 mark]*
Jeff didn't spend any time reading.

c) All we know is the proportion of time each person spent on an activity — the total amount of time they each spent on the activities could be different.
[1 mark]

2 a) She spends 5 + 3 + 1 + 3 = 12 hours doing these activities. So the multiplier is 360 ÷ 12 = 30.

Activity	Lessons	Meals	Homework	Hobbies
Time	5	3	1	3
Angle	5 × 30 = 150°	3 × 30 = 90°	1 × 30 = 30°	3 × 30 = 90°

[2 marks available — 1 mark for every 2 correct angles]

b)

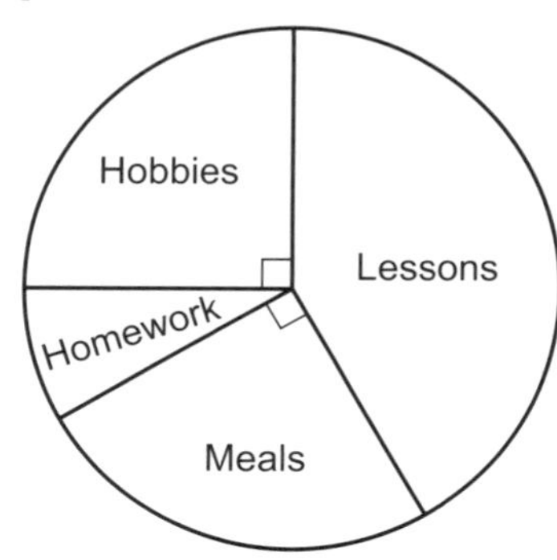

[2 marks available — 2 marks for a completely correct pie chart, otherwise 1 mark for 2 sectors correct]

Answers: P70 — P75

Page 70 — Mean, Median, Mode and Range

1 a) 8 – 1 = 7 ***[1 mark]***

b) 4 ***[1 mark]***

c) (4 + 7 + 3 + 1 + 4 + 6 + 8 + 4 + 5 + 7 + 5 + 6) ÷ 12
= 60 ÷ 12
= 5 ***[1 mark]***

2 a) (3 + (–3) + 4 + 0 + (–1) + 2 + 4) ÷ 7
= 9 ÷ 7 = 1.2857...°C
= 1.29 °C (2 d.p.) ***[1 mark]***

b) Write the temperatures in numerical order:
-3, -1, 0, 2, 3, 4, 4
The median temperature is the $\frac{7+1}{2}$ = 4th temperature.
Median = 2°C
[2 marks available — 2 marks for correct answer, otherwise 1 mark for finding the median is the 4th temperature.]

3 The mean is 16. The first score (14) is 2 less than the mean. The second score (16) is equal to the mean. So the third score must be 2 more than the mean.
16 + 2 = 18 ***[1 mark]***
You can check your answer by adding up the 3 test scores and dividing by 3 — it should give you 16.

Page 71 — Averages from Frequency Tables

1 a) Discrete ***[1 mark]***

b)

Number of Pets	Number of Families	No. of Pets × No. of Families
0	2	0
1	6	6
2	8	16
3	9	27
4	2	8
TOTAL	27	57

[2 marks available — 2 marks for a completely correct table, otherwise 1 mark for at least 4 correct entries]

c) $\frac{57}{27}$ = 2.111... = 2.1 (1 d.p.) ***[1 mark]***

2 a)

Number of devices	Frequency	Number of devices × Frequency
1	55	55
2	68	136
3	75	225
4	25	100
5	15	75
6	8	48
7	4	28
TOTAL	250	667

[2 marks available — 2 marks for a completely correct table, otherwise 1 mark for at least 4 correct entries]

b) $\frac{667}{250}$ = 2.7 (to 1 d.p.) ***[1 mark]***

Page 72 — Scatter Graphs

1 a) 1.7 m ***[1 mark]***

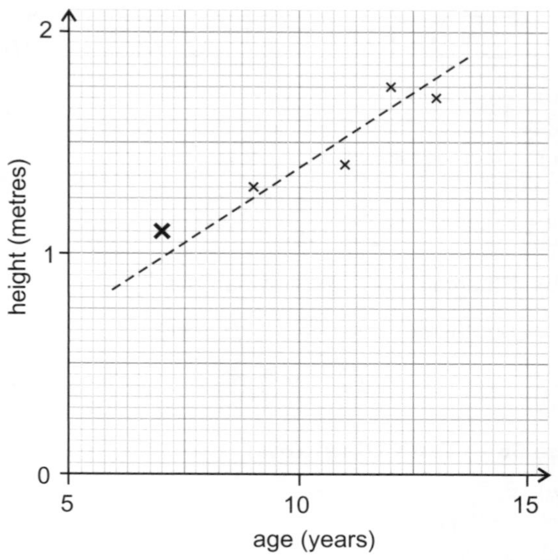

b) ***[1 mark for correctly plotting the point]***

c) ***[1 mark for line of best fit]***

d) The older the sibling, the taller they tend to be. ***[1 mark]***

2 a) Sales of hot chocolate — C
Sales of ice-pops — A
Sales of crisps — B
[2 marks available — 2 marks for all correct, otherwise 1 mark for 1 correct]

b) Diagram C shows a weak negative correlation. ***[1 mark]***

Practice Paper 1 — Calculator NOT allowed

1 a) 74 + 8 = 82 ***[1 mark]***

b) 9 × 5 = 45 ***[1 mark]***

2 ***[1 mark]***

3 a) 370, 469, 3071, 3459 ***[1 mark]***

b) 0.06, 0.136, 0.603, 0.65 ***[1 mark]***

4 a) There are 7 + 3 = 10 people in the tutor group.
The probability the chosen pupil is a boy is $\frac{7}{10}$. ***[1 mark]***

b) The probability the chosen pupil is a girl is $\frac{3}{10}$. ***[1 mark]***

5 a)
  1.9 5
+ 1.1 5
  3.1 0 so it will cost him £3.10. ***[1 mark]***

b)
  5.0 0
– 3.1 0
  1.9 0 so he will get £1.90 change. ***[1 mark]***

6 a) Square ***[1 mark]***

b) Rhombus ***[1 mark]***

c) Parallelogram ***[1 mark]***

Answers: P76 — P81

7 a) £12 ***[1 mark]***

b) 6 lengths ***[1 mark]***

8 17, 21 ***[1 mark]***

The rule for the sequence is "add 4 to the previous number".

48, 96 ***[1 mark]***

The rule for the sequence is "multiply the previous number by 2".

9 a) $30\% = \frac{30}{100} = \frac{3}{10}$ ***[1 mark]***

b) $\frac{2}{5} = \frac{4}{10} = \frac{40}{100} = 40\%$ ***[1 mark]***

c) Sebastian eats a quarter = 25% ***[1 mark]***
30% + 25% + 40% = 95% is eaten,
so 100% – 95% = 5% isn't eaten. ***[1 mark]***

10 a) A, C and E ***[1 mark]***

Teams with a negative goal difference will have let in more goals than they scored.

b) Team A lose by 5 goals so their goal difference will be 5 less: -9 – 5 = -14 ***[1 mark]***

Team C win by 5 goals so their goal difference will be 5 more: -4 + 5 = 1 ***[1 mark]***

11 a) The marks are in increasing order, so the median is halfway between 7 and 8:
(7 + 8) ÷ 2 = 7.5 ***[1 mark]***

b) The range is 5 so the other mark is 10 – 5 = 5. ***[1 mark]***

The other mark is NOT 8 + 5 = 13 as the test is only out of 10.

c) In size order he got the following marks over the two months: 5, 5, 7, 8, 8, 8, 10, 10.
So his modal mark was 8. ***[1 mark]***

12 a) $p = 180° – 50° = 130°$ ***[1 mark]***

Angles on a straight line add up to 180°.

b) $q = 50°$ ***[1 mark]***

Isosceles triangles have two equal angles.

c) $r = 180° – 50° – 50° = 80°$ ***[1 mark]***

Angles in a triangle add up to 180°.

13 a)

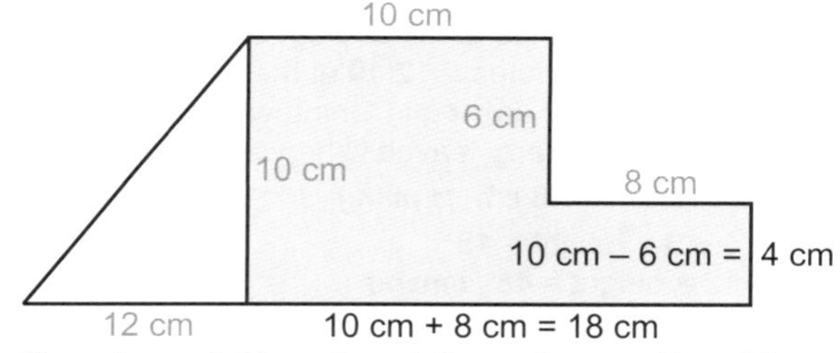

[2 marks available — 1 mark for each correct length]

b) Split it into a square and a rectangle:

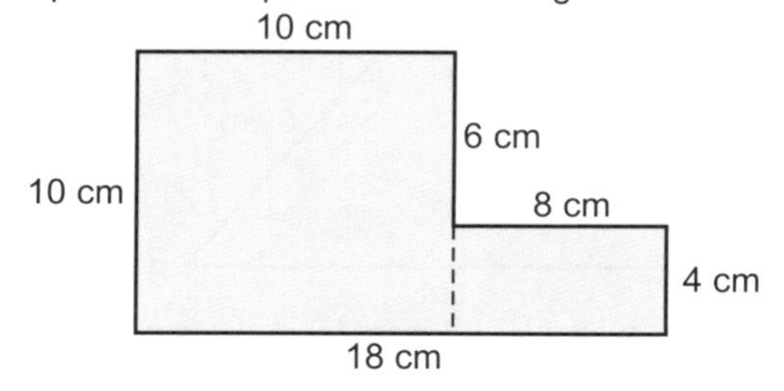

Area of square: 10 cm × 10 cm = 100 cm²
Area of rectangle: 8 cm × 4 cm = 32 cm²
Total area = 100 cm² + 32 cm² = 132 cm²

[2 marks available — 2 marks for the correct answer, otherwise 1 mark for splitting the shape up and finding the area of one part correctly]

You could have split the shape up horizontally to leave one 10 cm × 6 cm rectangle and one 18 cm × 4 cm rectangle.

c) Area of triangle = $\frac{1}{2}$ × 10 cm × 12 cm = 60 cm² ***[1 mark]***
Total area = 132 cm² + 60 cm² = 192 cm² ***[1 mark]***

14 a) $5a$ ***[1 mark]***

b) $12b^2$ ***[1 mark]***

c) $3(2c – 5) + 2c = 6c – 15 + 2c$ ***[1 mark]***
$= 8c – 15$ ***[1 mark]***

15 a)

Number of cups of tea	Tally	Frequency
0	III	3
1	IIII	4
2	~~IIII~~ I	6
3	IIII	4
4	III	3

[1 mark]

b)

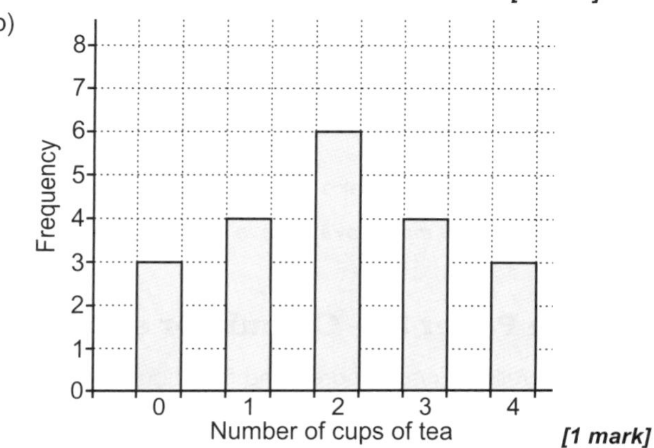

[1 mark]

c) There were 4 + 3 = 7 days out of 20 when Penny drank more than 2 cups of tea.
This is $\frac{7}{20}$ as a fraction. ***[1 mark]***

16 $2x + 15 = 5x$
$2x + 15 – 2x = 5x – 2x$
$15 = 3x$ ***[1 mark]***
$15 ÷ 3 = 3x ÷ 3$
$x = 5$ ***[1 mark]***

17 a) The side length of the table is 2 cm. ***[1 mark]***
So the real-life side length is 2 × 100 = 200 cm
= 2 m ***[1 mark]***

b) (i) Real-life length of sofa: 3 m = 300 cm
Length on drawing: 300 cm ÷ 100 = 3 cm ***[1 mark]***
Real-life width of sofa: 1 m = 100 cm
Width on drawing: 100 cm ÷ 100 = 1 cm ***[1 mark]***

(ii)

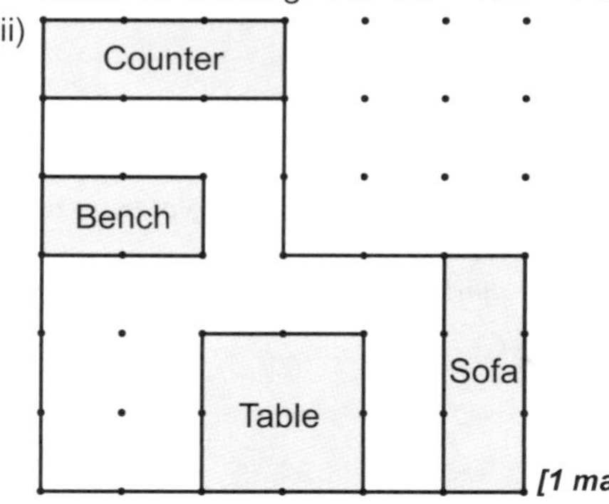

[1 mark]

18 a) 1 mile = 1.6 km so the conversion factor is 1.6.
100 miles × 1.6 = 160 km ***[1 mark]***

b) 160 km ÷ 8 hours = 20 km/h ***[1 mark]***

Answers: P82 — P88

19 Exterior angle = 360° ÷ number of sides
So x = 360° ÷ 6 = 60°. ***[1 mark]***
Interior angle = 180° – exterior angle
So y = 180° – 60° = 120°. ***[1 mark]***

20 a) plain flour : yeast
÷6 (600 g : 6 g) ÷6
100 g : 1 g = 100 : 1 ***[1 mark]***

b) Three pizza bases: 60 ml of milk.
One pizza base: 60 ml ÷ 3 = 20 ml of milk.
Nine pizza bases: 20 ml × 9 = 180 ml of milk.
[2 marks available — 2 marks for correct answer, otherwise 1 mark for finding amount needed for one pizza base]

c) 1 litre = 1000 ml so the conversion factor is 1000.
1.2 litres = 1.2 × 1000 = 1200 ml. ***[1 mark]***
water : plain flour
×4 (300 ml : 600 g) ×4
1200 ml : 2400 g
So 2400 g of plain flour is needed. ***[1 mark]***

d) Three pizza bases: 6 g of yeast.
One pizza base: 6 g ÷ 3 = 2 g of yeast. ***[1 mark]***
24 ÷ 2 = 12, so
24 g of yeast will make 12 pizza bases. ***[1 mark]***

[There are 60 marks available in total for Paper 1]

Practice Paper 2 — Calculator allowed

1 a) Two million, one hundred and fifty thousand, seven hundred and three. ***[1 mark]***
b) 50 000 ***[1 mark]***

2 a) 1000 – 427 = 573 ***[1 mark]***
b) 1000 ÷ 25 = 40 ***[1 mark]***
c) 850 ÷ 2 = 425 and 960 ÷ 3 = 320 ***[1 mark]***
425 – 320 = 105 ***[1 mark]***

3

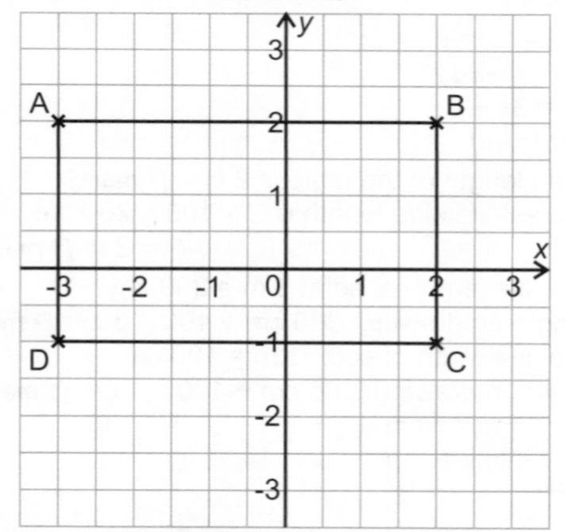

a) ***[2 marks available — 2 marks for a correctly drawn shape, otherwise 1 mark for plotting at least two points correctly]***
b) Rectangle ***[1 mark]***

4 a)

Friday	
Saturday	
Sunday	
Monday	***[1 mark]***

b) There are 3 + 4 + 2.5 + 2 = 11.5 symbols.
11.5 × 20 = 230 miles ***[1 mark]***

5 a) 12 000 ***[1 mark]***
b) 11 600 ***[1 mark]***

6 a) 6, 12, 18, 24, 30, 36 ***[1 mark]***
b) 9, 18, 27, 36, 45, 54 ***[1 mark]***
c) 18 ***[1 mark]***
The smallest number that appears in both lists.

7 a) 4°C ***[1 mark]***
b) -8°C ***[1 mark]*** *The minimum temperature on day 5.*
c) Day 4 ***[1 mark]***
The day with the largest gap between min and max temp.

8 Gym: £4.50 × 21 = £94.50
Pool: £2.20 × 28 = £61.60
Gym and Pool: £5.50 × 12 = £66.00
Total: £94.50 + £61.60 + £66.00 = £222.10
[2 marks available — 2 marks for the correct answer, otherwise 1 mark for working out at least two individual amounts correctly]

9 a) 30 minutes ***[1 mark]***
Ferries leave each place at 30 minute intervals.
b) 10:20 + 40 minutes = 11:00
11:00 + 33 minutes = 11:33
40 minutes + 33 minutes = 73 minutes ***[1 mark]***
c) She needs to be at the dock at Grimtown at
12:15 – 5 minutes = 12:10 at the latest.
The last ferry arriving in Grimtown before 12:10 is at 12:03. This ferry leaves Utherwaite at 11:48. ***[1 mark]***

10 a) 6 × 2 × 4 = 48 cm^3 ***[1 mark]***
b) 4 × 3 × height = 48
12 × height = 48 ***[1 mark]***
12 × height ÷ 12 = 48 ÷ 12
height = 4 cm ***[1 mark]***

11 a) E.g.

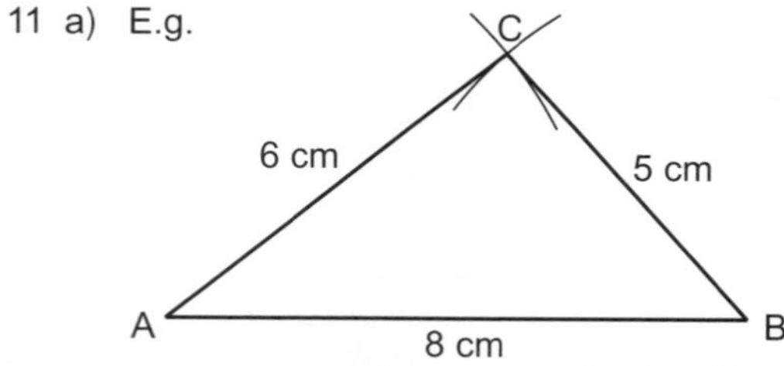

[3 marks available — 1 mark for drawing one side accurately, 1 mark for the correct construction lines, 1 mark for an accurate and correctly labelled triangle]
b) 93° ***[1 mark for any answer from 92° to 94°]***

Answers: P88 — P92

12 a)

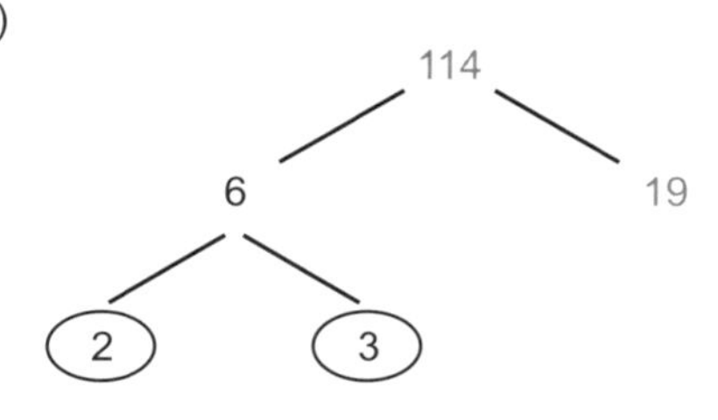

[2 marks available — 1 mark for getting "6", 1 mark for splitting 6 into its prime factors]

b) $2 \times 3 \times 19$ ***[1 mark]***

13 a) $240 - 80 - 50 - 90 = 20$ pupils only do French. ***[1 mark]***

b)

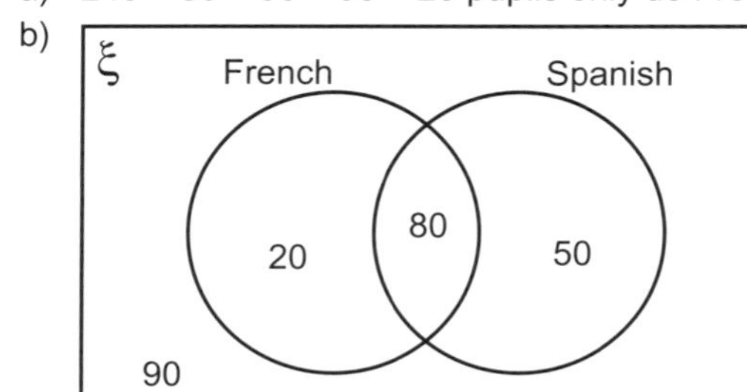

[2 marks available — 1 mark for two values in the correct places on the Venn diagram, 1 mark for the other two values in the correct places]

14 a) Angle a and angle FCD are corresponding angles so they are equal ***[1 mark]***. $a = 120°$ ***[1 mark]***

b) Angle b and angle ADC are alternate angles so they are equal ***[1 mark]***. $b = 141°$ ***[1 mark]***

15 a)

x	0	2	4
y	$(2 \times 0) - 1 = -1$	$(2 \times 2) - 1 = 3$	$(2 \times 4) - 1 = 7$

[1 mark]

b)

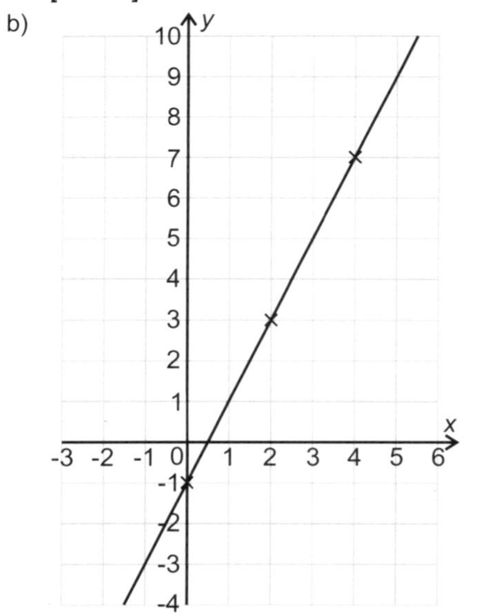

[1 mark for a straight line passing through each point from the table]

c) (0.5, 0) ***[1 mark]***

16 a) $1.5 \text{ m} \times 2 = 3 \text{ m}$ ***[1 mark]***

b) $3 \text{ m} \times \pi = 9.4247... \text{ m}$
$= 9$ m to the nearest m ***[1 mark]***

17 a) $30\% = 30 \div 100 = 0.3$
$0.3 \times £14.20 = £4.26$ ***[1 mark]***

b) $20\% = 20 \div 100 = 0.2$
$0.2 \times £38.10 = £7.62$ ***[1 mark]***
$£38.10 - £7.62 = £30.48$ ***[1 mark]***
You could also do $(1 - 0.2) \times £38.10 = 0.8 \times £38.10 = £30.48$

18 a)

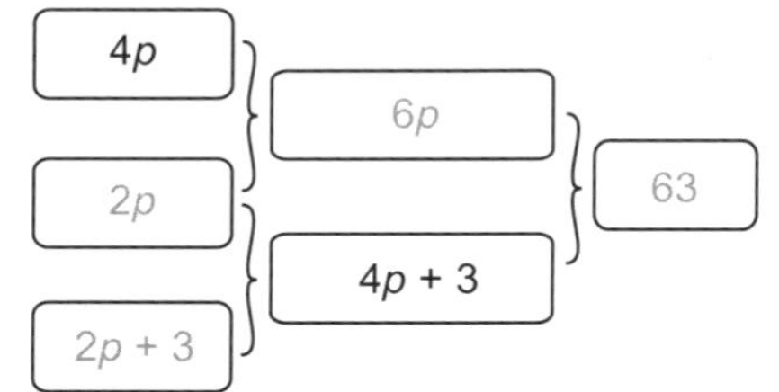

[2 marks available — 1 mark for filling in each box with the correct expression]

b) Using the 2nd and 3rd columns of the diagram:
$6p + 4p + 3 = 63$
$10p + 3 = 63$ ***[1 mark]***
$10p + 3 - 3 = 63 - 3$
$10p = 60$ ***[1 mark]***
$10p \div 10 = 60 \div 10$
$p = 6$ ***[1 mark]***

19 a)

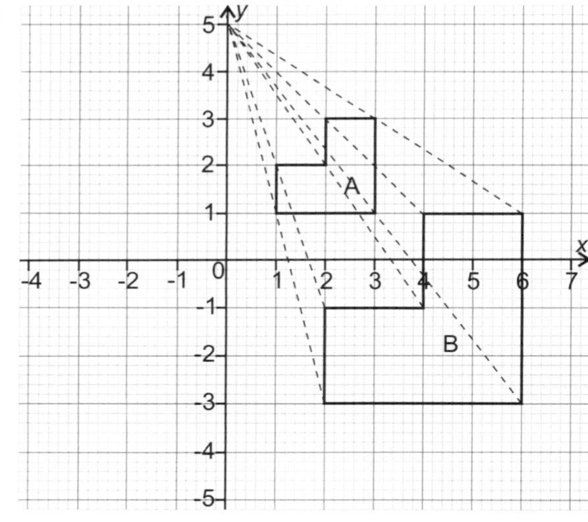

Shape B is an enlargement of shape A by scale factor 2 ***[1 mark]*** with centre of enlargement (0, 5). ***[1 mark]***
Sides of shape B are twice as long as sides in shape A and the lines through matching corners of the two shapes cross at (0, 5).

b) Similar ***[1 mark]***
They have the same shape but not the same size.

20 a) $360° - 160° - 90° - 70° = 40°$ ***[1 mark]***

b) $160° = 64$ trees
$1° = 64 \div 160 = 0.4$ trees ***[1 mark]***
$360° = 0.4 \times 360 = 144$ trees ***[1 mark]***

[There are 60 marks available in total for Paper 2]

ISBN 978 1 78294 173 6
9 781782 941736

MFQA32 £2.00 (Retail Price)

www.cgpbooks.co.uk

CHRIST
AMIGURUMI

Sayjai Thawornsupacharoen

From the series : Sayjai's Amigurumi Crochet Patterns, volume 6
K and J Publishing, 16 Whitegate Close, Swavesey, Cambridge CB24 4TT, England

Contents

2	Introduction
3	Little Gnomes and Mushroom Houses
8	Christmas Cuties
17	Christmas Girl
21	Santa, Snowman and Christmas Tree
27	How to join Yarn
27	How to read pattern
28	Copyright

For the first round: you can do 6 sc in magic ring instead of "Ch 2, 6 sc in second chain from hook."

Introduction

Christmas Amigurumi is a collection of cute and Christmassy crochet patterns. You need a basic knowledge of crochet to read the patterns.

Size

You can make the doll smaller or bigger by using different yarn and hook, without changing a pattern.

- The small dolls are 1.8 to 2.6 inches (4.5 to 6.5 cm) high.
- The big dolls are 5 to 8.5 inches (12.5 cm to 21.5 cm) high.

The size of the doll depends on the size of the crochet hook, the thickness of yarn and how you stuff it; a bigger hook and thicker yarn make a bigger doll. A doll stuffed tightly is bigger than a loose stuffed doll.

Abbreviations

This book uses USA crochet terminology.

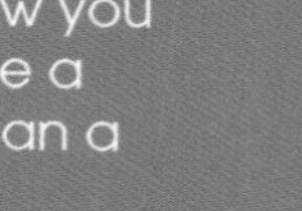

ch = chain
sc = single crochet
hdc = half double crochet
dc = double crochet
lp st = loop stitch
st = stitch
sl = slip
rnd = round
tog = together

Conversion chart for USA/ UK crochet abbreviations:

USA Crochet Abbreviations	UK Crochet Abbreviations
sc = single crochet	dc = double crochet
hdc = half double crochet	htr = half treble crochet
dc = double crochet	tr = treble crochet

Little Gnomes & Mushroom Houses

Big, Small and Medium

You can make the gnomes and mushrooms bigger or smaller, without changing the patterns.
The big gnome is about 5 inches/ 12.5 cm high.
The big mushroom house is 7 inches/ 17.5 cm high.

The size of the dolls depend on the size of crochet hook, thickness of yarn and how you stuff them; a bigger hook and thicker yarn make bigger gnomes. A gnome stuffed tightly is bigger than a loosely stuffed gnome.

The big gnome and big mushroom house:
I used a 5.5 mm hook and No 5 yarn (Bulky, Chunky, Craft, Rug): Sirdar Hayfield Bonus Chunky.

The medium size:
I used a 4.5 mm hook and No 3 yarn (DK): Schachenmayr Cotton Time, Metallic yarn Twilley's Goldfingering (crochet them together; one cotton and one metallic).

The smallest size:
I used a 3 mm hook and No 2 yarn (Sport, Baby): Schachenmayr Catania, DMC Petra.

EASY

Size

Big Gnome: 5 inches/ 12.5 cm high.
Big Mushroom House: 7 inches/ 17.5 cm high.

Materials

Materials for making 4 big Gnomes and 1 big Mushroom House.

- Bulky, Chunky, Craft, Rug (BULKY 5)
  Sirdar Hayfield Bonus Chunky:
  White 961 = 10 g, Wheat 816 (Beige color) = 55 g, Lime Green 785 = 25 g, Black 965 = 15 g, Signal Red 977= 55 g and Cinder 786 = 30 g
- 5.5 mm hook (US: I/9, UK: 5)
- One Black 5 mm bead for door knob
- Tapestry needle
- Needle and thread for sewing nose
- Plastic Pellets = 12 oz (340 g)
- Polyester fibrefill = 60 g
- Comb or a wire brush (a yarn indicator brush)

Remarks

This project is working in continuous rounds, do not join or turn unless otherwise stated. Mark first stitch of each round.

Gnome

Body

Rnd 1: With **Red 977** (body color), ch 2, 6 sc in second chain from hook. (6)
Rnd 2: 2 sc in each st around. (12)
Rnd 3: (2 sc in next st, sc in next st) around. (18)
Rnd 4: (Sc in next 2 sts, 2 sc in next st) around. (24)
Rnd 5: Working in back loops only. Sc in each st around. (24)
Rnd 6: Sc in next 3 sts, sc next 2 sts tog, (sc in next 6 sts, sc next 2 sts tog) 2 times, sc in next 3 sts. (21)
Rnd 7: Sc in each st around. (21)
Rnd 8: (Sc in next 5 sts, sc next 2 sts tog) around. (18)
Rnd 9: Sc in each st around. (18)
Rnd 10: Sc in next 2 sts, sc next 2 sts tog, (sc in next 4 sts, sc next 2 sts tog) 2 times, sc in next 2 sts. (15)
Rnd 11: Sc in each st around. (15)
Rnd 12: (Sc in next 3 sts, sc next 2 sts tog) around. (12)
Rnd 13: Sc in each st around. (12)
Rnd 14: (Sc in next 2 sts, sc next 2 sts tog) around. Fill ¾ of body with Plastic pellets then stuff with Polyester fibrefill. (9)
* Use funnel for filling Plastic pellets.*
Rnd 15: (Sc in next st, sc next 2 sts tog) around, join with sl st in first st, leave long end for sewing, fasten off. Stuff more with Polyester fibrefill by using tip of scissors, sew the opening close. (6)

Hat

Rnd 1: With **Red 977** (hat color), ch 2, 3 sc in second chain from hook. (3)
Rnd 2: 2 sc in each st around. (6)
Rnd 3: (2 sc in next st, sc in next st) around. (9)
Rnd 4: Sc in each st around. (9)
Rnd 5: (Sc in next 2 sts, 2 sc in next st) around. (12)
Rnd 6: Sc in each st around. (12)
Rnd 7: (2 sc in next st, sc in next 3 sts) around. (15)
Rnd 8: Sc in each st around. (15)
Rnd 9: Sc in next 2 sts, 2 sc in next st, (sc in next 4 sts, 2 sc in next st) 2 times, sc in next 2 sts. (18)
Rnd 10-11: Sc in each st around. (18)

First Ear Flap

Rows 12-17 are working in rows.
Row 12: Sc in next 5 sts, turn. (5)
Row 13-15: Ch 1, sc in each st across, turn. (5)
Row 16: Ch 1, sc first 2 sts tog, sc in next st, sc next 2 sts tog, turn. (3)
Row 17: Ch 1, sc 3 sts tog, fasten off. (1)

Second Ear Flap

Rows 12-17 are working in rows.
Row 12: Join **Red** to the fifth st from the first ear flap on Rnd 11, ch 1, sc in same st, sc in next 4 sts, turn. (5)
The space between ear flaps are 4 sts.
Row 13-15: Ch 1, sc in each st across, turn. (5)
Row 16: Ch 1, sc first 2 sts tog, sc in next st, sc next 2 sts tog, turn. (3)
Row 17: Ch 1, sc 3 sts tog, fasten off. (1)

Beard

Cut 6 strands of **White** yarn, 6 inches long. Tie them together in the middle, brush them with comb or wire brush. Sew / attach beard to rnd 13 of body.

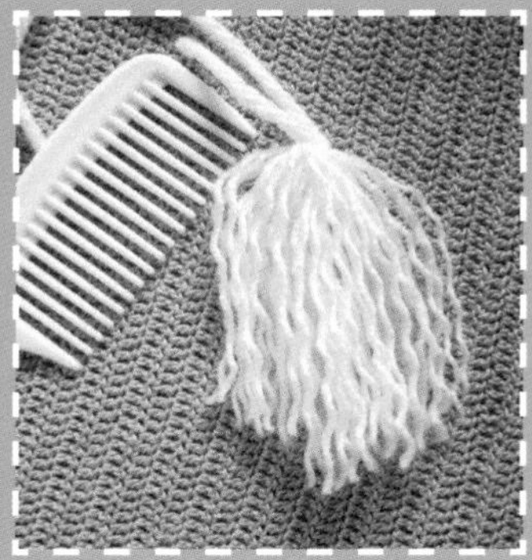

Nose

You can use 10 mm bead for nose instead of crocheted nose.

With **Beige** (nose color), ch 2, 6 sc in second chain from hook, join with sl st in first st, fasten off. (6)
Use needle and thread to sew the edge together to make a ball.

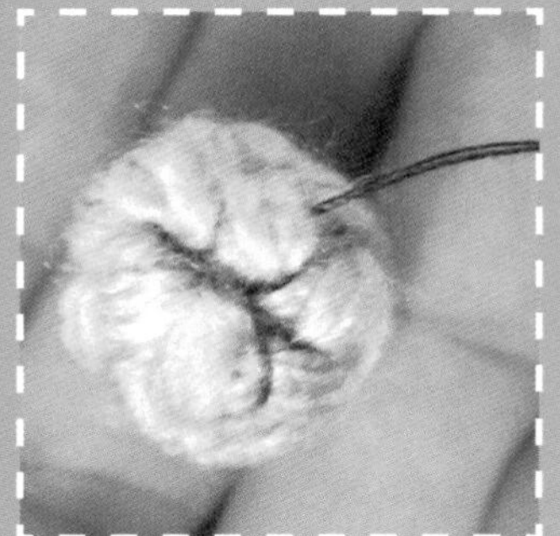

Sew nose on body on top of the beard.

Foot

Make 2.
Rnd 1: With **Black 965**, ch 2, 6 sc in second chain from hook. (6)
Rnd 2: (2 sc in next st, sc in next st) around. (9)
Rnd 3: Sc in each st around. (9)
Rnd 4: Sc in each st around, join with sl st in first st, leave long end for sewing, fasten off. (9)
Stuff foot and sew the opening close.

Sew feet to free loops of rnd 4 of the body.

Mushroom House

Cap

Rnd 1: **With Red 977**, ch 2, 6 sc in second chain from hook. (6)
Rnd 2: 2 sc in each st around. (12)
Rnd 3: (2 sc in next st, sc in next st) around. (18)
Rnd 4: (Sc in next 2 sts, 2 sc in next st) around. (24)
Rnd 5: (Sc in next 3 sts, 2 sc in next st) around. (30)
Rnd 6: Sc in next 2 sts, 2 sc in next st, (sc in next 4 sts, 2 sc in next st) 5 times, sc in next 2 sts. (36)
Rnd 7: (Sc in next 11 sts, 2 sc in next st) around. (39)
Rnd 8: Sc in next 6 sts, 2 sc in next st, (sc in next 12 sts, 2 sc in next st) 2 times, sc in next 6 sts. (42)
Rnd 9: Sc in next 3 sts, 2 sc in next st, (sc in next 6 sts, 2 sc in next st) 5 times, sc in next 3 sts. (48)
Rnd 10: (Sc in next 15 sts, 2 sc in next st) around. (51)
Rnd 11: Sc in next 8 sts, 2 sc in next st, (sc in next 16 sts, 2 sc in next st) 2 times, sc in next 8 sts. (54)
Rnd 12-14: Sc in each st around. (54)
Rnd 15: Working in back loops only. (Sc next 2 sts tog, sc in next 7 sts) around, changing to **Wheat 816** (Beige, stem color) in last 2 loops of last st. (48)
Rnd 16: Sc in next 2 sts, sc next 2 sts tog, (sc in next 4 sts, sc next 2 sts tog) 7 times, sc in next 2 sts. (40)
Rnd 17: (Sc in next 3 sts, sc next 2 sts tog) around, sl st in first st, fasten off. Stuff the cap. (32)

Stem

Rnd 1: With **Wheat 816** (Beige, stem color), ch 2, 6 sc in second chain from hook. (6)
Rnd 2: 2 sc in each st around. (12)
Rnd 3: (2 sc in next st, sc in next st) around. (18)
Rnd 4: (Sc in next 2 sts, 2 sc in next st) around. (24)
Rnd 5: (Sc in next 3 sts, 2 sc in next st) around. (30)
Rnd 6: Sc in next 2 sts, 2 sc in next st, (sc in next 4 sts, 2 sc in next st) 5 times, sc in next 2 sts. (36)
Rnd 7: (Sc in next 5 sts, 2 sc in next st) around. (42)
Rnd 8: Sc in next 3 sts, 2 sc in next st, (sc in next 6 sts, 2 sc in next st) 5 times, sc in next 3 sts. (48)
Rnd 9-14: Sc in each st around. (48)
Rnd 15: Sc next 7 sts, sc next 2 sts tog, (sc in next 14 sts, sc next 2 sts tog) 2 times, sc in next 7 sts. (45)
Rnd 16: Sc in each st around. (45)
Rnd 17: (Sc in next 13 sts, sc next 2 sts tog) around. (42)
Rnd 18: Sc in each st around. (42)
Rnd 19: Sc in next 6 sts, sc next 2 sts tog, (sc in next 12 sts, sc next 2 sts tog) 2 times, sc in next 6 sts. (39)
Rnd 20: Sc in each st around. (39)

Rnd 21: (Sc in next 11 sts, sc next 2 sts tog) around. (36)
Rnd 22: Sc in each st around. (36)
Rnd 23: Sc in next 5 sts, sc next 2 sts tog, (sc in next 10 sts, sc next 2 sts tog) 2 times, sc in next 5 sts. (33)
Rnd 24: Sc in each st around, join with sl st in first st, leave long end for sewing, fasten off. (33)

Door

Row 1: With **Red 977**, ch 7, sc in second chain from hook, sc in next 5 sts, turn. (6)
Row 2-5: Ch 1, sc in each st across, turn. (6)
Row 6: Ch 1, sc first 2 sts tog, sc in next 2 sts, sc next 2 sts tog, turn. (4)
Row 7: Ch 1, sc first 2 sts tog, sc in next 2 sts tog, leave long end for sewing, fasten off. (2)

Sew bead on rnd 4 of door (door knob), then sew door on rnds 9-16 of stem.

Door Frame

With **Lime Green 785**, ch 20, leave long end for sewing, fasten off. Sew it around door.

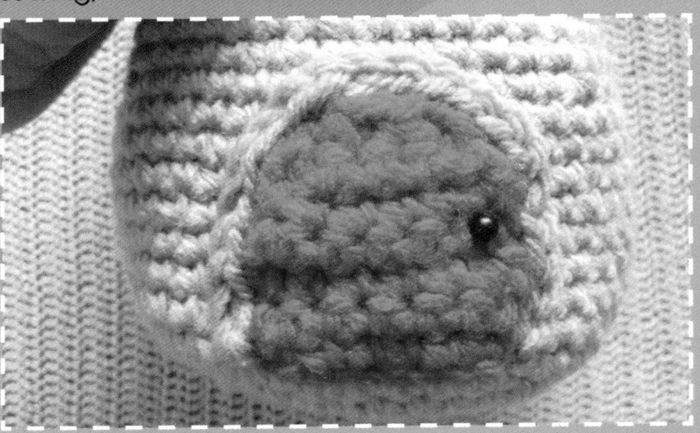

Fill stem with 8 oz (227 g) plastic pellets then stuff with polyester fibrefill. Sew stem to cap and stuff more tightly before sewing the opening close.

White Spots on top of Cap

Make 3.
Rnd 1: With **White 961**, Ch 2, 6 sc in second chain from hook. (6)
Rnd 2: 2 sc in each st around, leave long end for sewing, fasten off. (12)

Sew White spots on top of cap as in pictures.

Christmas Cuties

Size

- The Dolls are 2.4 inches/ 6 cm high excluding hat. (Snowman, Santa Claus, Deer, Gingerbread man, Penguin, Robin, Polar Bear)
- The Star is 2.6 inches/ 6.5 cm.
- The Sock is 2.4 inches/ 6cm high.
- The Heart is 1.8 inches/ 4.5 cm high.
- The Wreath is 1.8 inches/ 4.5 cm diameter.
- Christmas Pudding is 2 inches/ 5 cm high and 2 inches/ 5 cm diameter.

Materials

- No 2 yarn (Sport, Baby). Catania yarn from Schachenmayr SMC one 50 g ball each (color: white 106, black 110, cream 130, red 115, green 241, dark brown 162, taupe 254 and yellow 208).
- 3.25 mm hook (US: D/3.25, UK: 10)
- 7 pairs of black 4 mm beads for doll eyes
- Seven 10 mm bells
- Polyester fibrefill = 50 g
- Tapestry needle
- Sewing needle and thread for attaching doll eyes and bells
- Pins

Star

Make 2.

Rnd 1: With color **Yellow 208**, Ch 2, 5 sc in second chain from hook. (5)
Rnd 2: 2 sc in each st around. (10)
Rnd 3: (Sc in next st, 2 sc in next st) around. (15)
Rnd 4: (Sc in next 2 sts, 2sc in next st) around. (20)

Working in rows.
Row 5: First point, sc in next 4 sts, turn. (4)
Row 6: Ch 1, sc first 2 sts tog, sc next 2 sts tog, turn. (2)
Row 7: Ch 1, sc in each st across, turn. (2)
Row 8: Ch 1, sc first 2 sts tog, fasten off.

Row 5: Second to fifth star point, join **Yellow 208** to next free st on rnd 4, ch 1, sc in same st, sc in next 3 sts,turn. (4)

Row 6: Ch 1, sc first 2 sts tog, sc next 2 sts tog, turn. (2)
Row 7: Ch 1, sc in each st across, turn. (2)
Row 8: Ch 1, sc first 2 sts tog, fasten off.

Finishing

Hold 2 pieces of star with wrong sides together, matching points; sew edge of star pieces together and make a loop on middle top for hanging.

Sock

Rnd 1: With color **Red 115**, ch 13, sc in second chain from hook, sc in next 10 chs, 3 sc in last ch; working in remaining loops on opposite side of chain, sc in next 10 chs, 2 sc in next ch. (26)

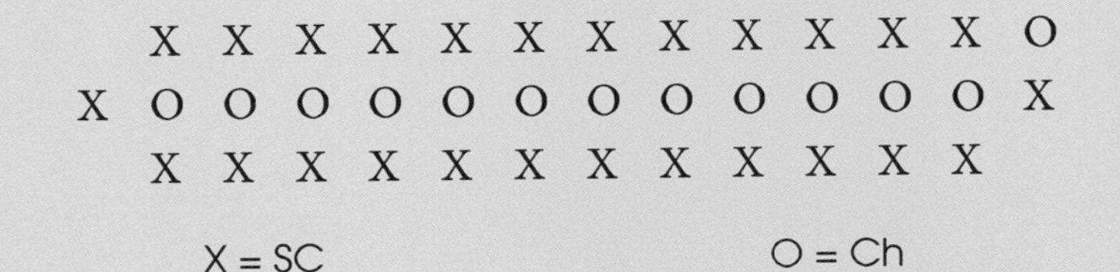

Rnd 2-4: Sc in each st around. (26)
Rnd 5: Sc in next 9 sts, (sc next 2 sts tog) 4 times, sc in next 9 sts. (22)
Rnd 6: Sc in next 7 sts, (sc next 2 sts tog) 4 times, sc in next 7 sts. (18)
Rnd 7: Sc in next 7 sts, (sc next 2 sts tog) 2 times, sc in next 7 sts. (16)
Rnd 8-9: Sc in each st around. (16)
Rnd 10: Sc in each st around, change to **White 106** in last 2 loops of last st. (16)
Rnd 11: Sc in each st around, change to **Red 115** in last 2 loops of last st. (16)
Rnd 12: Sc in each st around, change to **White 106** in last 2 loops of last st. (16)
Rnd 13: Sc in each st around, change to **Red 115** in last 2 loops of last st. (16)
Rnd 14: Sc in each st around. (16)
Rnd 15: Sc in each st around, join with sl st in first st, fasten off. (16)

Finishing
Make a loop on the sock for hanging.

Heart

Hump
Make 2.
Rnd 1: With color **Red 115**, ch 2, 5 sc in second chain from hook. (5)
Rnd 2: 2 sc in each st around. (10)
Rnd 3: (Sc in next st, 2 sc in next st) around. (15)

For first hump, join with sl st in first st. Fasten off.
For second hump, do not sl st in first st. Do not fasten off.
Rnd 4: With the right side facing you, sc in st on first hump (mark first st), sc in next 14 sts on first hump, sc in next 15 sts on second hump. (30)

Rnd 5: (Sc next 2 sts tog, sc in next 4 sts) around. (25)
Rnd 6: Sc in each st around. (25)
Rnd 7: (Sc next 2 sts tog, sc in next 3 sts) around. (20)
Rnd 8: Sc in each st around. (20)
Rnd 9: (Sc next 2 sts tog, sc in next 2 sts) around. (15)
Rnd 10: (Sc next 2 sts tog, sc in next st) around. (10)
Rnd 11: Sc next 2 sts tog around, join with sl st in first st. Fasten off. (5)

Finishing
Make a loop on middle for hanging.

Christmas Pudding

Pudding
Rnd 1: With color **Dark Brown162**, ch 2, 6 sc in second chain from hook. (6)
Rnd 2: 2 sc in each st around. (12)
Rnd 3: (Sc in next st, 2 sc in next st) around. (18)
Rnd 4: (2 sc in next st, sc in next 2 sts) around. (24)
Rnd 5: (Sc in next 3 sts, 2 sc in next st) around. (30)
Rnd 6: Working in back loops only. Sc in each st around. (30)
Rnd 7: Sc in each st around. (30)
Rnd 8: Sc in each st around, changing to **White 106** in last 2 loops of last st. (30)
Rnd 9: (Sc next 2 sts tog, sc in next 3 sts) around. (24)
Rnd 10: Working in back loops only. Sc in next 3 sts, sc next 2 sts tog, (sc in next 6 sts, sc next 2 sts tog) 2 times, sc in next 3 sts. (21)
Rnd 11: (Sc in next 5 sts, sc next 2 sts tog) around. (18)
Rnd 12: Sc in next 2 sts, sc next 2 sts tog, (sc in next 4 sts, sc next 2 sts tog) 2 times, sc in next 2 sts. (15)
Rnd 13: (Sc in next 3 sts, sc next 2 sts tog) around. Stuff. (12)

Rnd 14: Sc next 2 sts tog around, join with sl st in first st. Fasten off. (6)

Edge of pudding: Join **White** to free loops of rnd 9, sc in same st, (ch 3, sc in next st) around, fasten off.

Cherry

Rnd 1: With color **Red 115**, ch 2, 5 sc in second chain from hook. (5)
Rnd 2: 2 sc in each st around. (10)
Rnd 3: Sc in each st around. (10)
Rnd 4: Sc next 2 sts tog around, join with sl st in first st. Leave long end for sewing, fasten off. (5)

Stuff cherry by using tip of small scissors to push the stuffing in.

Leaf

With color **Green 241**, ch 5, sl st in second chain from hook, sc in next ch, dc in next ch, sc in next ch, leave long end for sewing, fasten off.

Finishing

Sew leaf on top of pudding, sew cherry on top of leaf. Make a loop on middle top for hanging.

Wreath

With color **Green 241**, ch 30, dc in 4th chain from hook, dc in next 26 chs, leave long end for sewing, fasten off.

Bow

With color **Red 115**, ch 30, fasten off. Tie a bow.

Finishing

Sew both ends together to make a circle, sew top of dc stitches to starting chains (see picture below). Sew bow on wreath and make a loop on middle top for hanging.

Doll Patterns

Remarks

The dolls have the same basic patterns; Head, Body and Hats.

Head and Body Pattern

Working from bottom of the Body to top of the Head.

Rnd 1: With color **White 106**, ch 2, 6 sc in second chain from hook. (6)
Rnd 2: 2 sc in each st around. (12)
Rnd 3-5: Sc in each st around.
Rnd 6: Sc next 2 sts tog around. (6)
Rnd 7: 2sc in each st around. (12)
Rnd 8: (Sc in next st, 2 sc in next st) around. (18)
Rnd 9: (Sc in next 2 sts, 2 sc in next st) around. (24)
Rnd 10-14: Sc in each st around.
Rnd 15: (Sc next 2 sts tog, sc in next 2 sts) around. Stuff. (18)
Rnd 16: (Sc next 2 sts tog, sc in next sts) around. (12)
Rnd 17: Sc next 2 sts tog around, sl st in first st. Fasten off. Sew opening close. (6)

Big Hat

For Santa Claus, Snowman, Gingerbread man, Penguin and Red Robin.

Rnd 1: With color **Red 115**, ch 2, 6 sc in second chain from hook. (6)
Rnd 2: Sc in each st around.
Rnd 3: (Sc in next st, 2 sc in next st) around. (9)
Rnd 4: (Sc in next 2 sts, 2 sc in next st) around. (12)
Rnd 5: (Sc in next 3 sts, 2 sc in next st) around. (15)
Rnd 6: Sc in each st around.
Rnd 7: (Sc in next 4 sts, 2 sc in next st) around. (18)
Rnd 8: (Sc in next 5 sts, 2 sc in next st) around. (21)
Rnd 9: (Sc in next 6 sts, 2 sc in next st) around. (24)
Rnd 10: (Sc in next 7 sts, 2 sc in next st) around. (27)
Rnd 11: (Sc in next 8 sts, 2 sc in next st) around, sl st in first st. Fasten off. (30)

Edge of Hat: Working in Rows.
Row 1: With color **Green 24**, ch 4, sc in second chain from hook, sc in next 3 chs, turn. (3)
Row 2-26: Working in back loops only; ch 1, sc in each st across, turn. (3)
Row 27: Working in back loops only; ch 1, sc in each st across. Leave long end for sewing, fasten off.

Sew row 1 and row 27 together to make a circle. Sew the Edge on rnd 11 of Hat. Sew Bell on top of the hat.

Small Hat

For Deer and Polar Bear.

Rnd 1: With color **Red 115**, ch 2, 6 sc in second chain from hook. (6)
Rnd 2: Sc in each st around.
Rnd 3: (Sc in next st, 2 sc in next st) around. (9)
Rnd 4: (Sc in next 2 sts, 2 sc in next st) around. (12)
Rnd 5: (Sc in next 3 sts, 2 sc in next st) around. (15)
Rnd 6: Sc in each st around, changing to **White 106** in last 2 loops of last st. (15)
Rnd 7: (Sc in next 4 sts, 2 sc in next st) around, sl st in first st, leave long end for sewing, fasten off. (18)

Sew Bell on hat and make a loop on top of the hat for hanging.

Santa Claus

Body and Head

Follow the instructions for the Doll Body and Head Pattern.

Rnds 1-6: color **Red 115**
Rnds 7-17: color **Cream 130**

Beard

Working in rows.
Row 1: With color **White 106**, ch 11, sc in second chain from hook, sc in next 9 chs, turn. (10)
Row 2: Ch 1, sc first 2 sts tog, sc in next 6 sts, sc next 2 sts tog, turn. (8)
Row 3: Ch 1, sc first 2 sts tog, sc in next 4 sts, sc next 2 sts tog, turn. (6)
Row 4: Ch 1, sc first 2 sts tog, sc in next 2 sts, sc next 2 sts tog, turn. (4)
Row 5: Ch 1, sc first 2 sts tog, sc next 2 sts tog, turn. (2)
Row 6: Ch 1, sc first 2 sts tog, fasten off. (1)

Hat

Follow the instructions for the Big Hat pattern.

Finishing

Sew eyes 4 sts apart between rnds 12-13 of head.
Sew beard on rnd 11.

With color **Red 115** embroider mouth on top row of beard (See page 27).
Put the Hat on and sew to head, make a loop on top of head for hanging.

Snowman and Gingerbread Man

Body and Head

Follow the instructions for the Dolls Body and Head Pattern.

Snowman: color **White 106.**

Gingerbread man: color **Taupe 254.**

Hat

Follow the instructions for the Big Hat pattern.

Scarf

With color **Red 115**, ch 30, fasten off.

Finishing

Sew eyes 4 sts apart between rnds 12-13 of head. With **Red** embroider mouth on rnd 11. Put the Hat on and sew to head, make a loop on top of head for hanging and tie the scarf around the neck.

Polar Bear

Body and Head

With color **White 106**, follow the instructions for the Dolls Body and Head Pattern.

Ear

Make 2.

Rnd 1: With color **White 106**, ch 2, 6 sc in second chain from hook. (6)

Rnd 2: Sc in each st around, sl st in first st, leave long end for sewing, fasten off. (6)

Hat

Follow the instructions for the Small Hat pattern.

Scarf

With color **Red 115**, ch 30, fasten off.

Finishing

Sew eyes 4 sts apart between rnds 12-13 of head. With color **Black 110** embroider mouth as in picture above. Sew ears on rnds 13-15 of head. Put the Hat on and sew to head and tie the scarf around the neck.

Deer

Body and Head
With color **Taupe 254**, Follow the instructions for the Dolls Body and Head Pattern.

Antler
Make 2.
With color **Dark Brown 162**, ch 7, sl st in second chain from hook, sl st in next ch, ch 4, sl st in second chain from hook, sl st in next 6 chs, leave long end for sewing, fasten off.

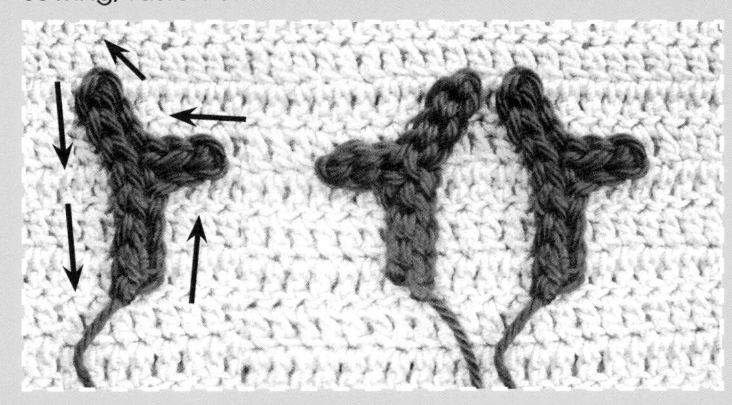

Hat
Follow the instructions for the Small Hat pattern.

Scarf
With color **Red 115**, ch 30, fasten off.

Finishing
Sew eyes 4 sts apart between rnds 12-13 of head. With color **Red 115** embroider mouth as in picture. Sew antlers on rnd 15 of head. Put the Hat on and sew to head, tie the scarf around the neck.

Red Robin

Body and Head
Follow the instructions for the Body and Head Pattern.

Rnds 1-6: color **Red 115**
Rnds 7-17: color **Taupe 254**

Beak
Rnd 1: With color **Yellow 208**, ch 2, 6 sc in second chain from hook. (6)
Rnd 2: Sc in each st around, sl st in first st, leave long end for sewing, fasten off. (6)

Wing
Make 2.
Rnd 1: With color **Dark Brown 162**, ch 2, 6 sc in second chain from hook. (6)
Rnd 2: (2 sc in next st, sc in next st) around. (9)
Rnd 3-4: Sc in each st around. (9)
Rnd 5: (Sc next 2 sts tog, sc in next st) around, leave long end for sewing, fasten off. (6)

Hat
Follow the instructions for the Big Hat pattern.

Finishing
Sew eyes 4 sts apart between rnds 12-13 of head. Sew beak between eyes. Sew wings on rnd 6 of body. Put the Hat on and sew to head, make a loop on top of head for hanging.

Penguin

Body and Head

Working from bottom of the Body to top of the Head.
Rnd 1: With color **White 106**, ch 2, 6 sc in second chain from hook. (6)
Rnd 2: 2 sc in each st around. (12)
Rnd 3-5: Sc in each st around.
Rnd 6: Sc next 2 sts tog around, changing to **Black 110** in last 3 loops of last st. (6)
Rnd 7: 2sc in next 2 sts, changing to **White 106**, 2 sc in next 2 sts, changing to **Black 110**, 2 sc in next 2 sts. (12)

V V V V V V
(V = 2 sc in same st)

Rnd 8: (Sc in next st, 2 sc in next st) 2 times, changing to **White 106**, 2 sc in next st, sc in next 2 sts, 2 sc in next st, changing to **Black 110**, (2 sc in next st, sc in next st) 2 times. (18)

X V X V V X X V V X V X
(X = sc)

Rnd 9: Sc in next 2 sts, 2 sc in next st, sc in next 2 sts, changing to **White 106**, 2 sc in next 2 sts, sc in next 4 sts, 2 sc in next 2 sts, changing to **Black 110**, sc in next 2 sts, 2 sc in next st, sc in next 2 sts. (24)

X X V X X V V X X X X V V X X V X X

Rnd 10-11: Sc in next 6 sts, changing to **White 106**, sc in next 5 sts, changing to **Black 110**, sc in next 2 sts, changing to **White 106**, sc in next 5 sts, changing to **Black 110**, sc in next 6 sts. (24)

X X X X X X X X X X X X X X X X X X X X X X X X

Rnd 12: Sc in next 7 sts, changing to **White 106**, sc in next 3 sts, changing to **Black 110**, sc in next 4 sts, changing to **White 106**, sc in next 3 sts, changing to **Black 110**, sc in next 7 sts. (24)

X X X X X X X X X X X X X X X X X X X X X X X X

Rnd 13-14: Sc in each st around. (24)
Rnd 15: (Sc next 2 sts tog, sc in next 2 sts) around. Stuff. (18)
Rnd 16: (Sc next 2 sts tog, sc in next sts) around. (12)
Rnd 17: Sc next 2 sts tog around, sl st in first st. Fasten off. Sew opening close. (6)

Beak

Rnd 1: With color **Yellow 208**, ch 2, 6 sc in second chain from hook. (6)
Rnd 2: Sc in each st around, sl st in first st, leave long end for sewing, fasten off. (6)

Wing

Make 2.
Rnd 1: With color **Black 110**, ch 2, 6 sc in second chain from hook. (6)
Rnd 2: (2 sc in next st, sc in next st) around. (9)
Rnd 3-4: Sc in each st around. (9)
Rnd 5: (Sc next 2 sts tog, sc in next st) around, leave long end for sewing, fasten off. (6)

Hat

Follow the instructions for the Big Hat pattern.

Finishing

Sew eyes 4 sts apart between rnds 10-11 of head. Sew beak between eyes. Sew wings on rnd 6 of body.

Put the Hat on and sew to head, make a loop on top of head for hanging.

Christmas Girl

Size

High 8.5 inches / 21.5 cm.

Materials

- Sport, 4 ply yarn
  Colors: Cream, Red and Green
- 3.00 mm hook
- Fine Mohair yarn (Peach for hair)
- One small bell
- Polyester fiberfill
- Black 8 mm buttons for eyes or other eyes as desired
- Tapestry needle
- Sewing needle and thread for attaching eyes

Foot and Leg

Make 2.

Rnd 1: With **Red**, ch 2, 6 sc in second ch from hook.(6)
Rnd 2: 2 sc in each st around. (12)
Rnd 3: (Sc in next st, 2 sc in next st) around. (18)
Rnd 4: Working in back loops only. Sc in each st around.
Rnd 5: Sc in next 6 sts, (sc next 2 sts tog) 3 times, sc in next 6 sts. (15)
Rnd 6: Sc in next 3 sts, (sc next 2 sts tog) 2 times, sc in next st, (sc next 2 sts tog) 2 times, sc in next 3 sts. (11)
Rnd 7-8: Sc in each st around, changing to **Green** in last 2 loops of last st.
Rnd 9: Sc in each st around, changing to **Cream** in last 2 loops of last st.
Rnd 10: Working in back loops only. Sc in each st around. Stuff.
Rnd 11-24: Sc in each st around.
Rnd 25: Sc in each st around, join with sl st in first st. Fasten off.

Body and Head

Rnd 1: With **Cream**, hold legs together with upper inner thighs together and toes pointed forward. Insert hook in the center on innermost thigh of first leg, pull out the loop from second leg, ch 1, sc in same st (do not count this st just for connecting legs together), sc in next 10 sts on second leg (mark first st), sc in next 10 sts on first leg. (20)

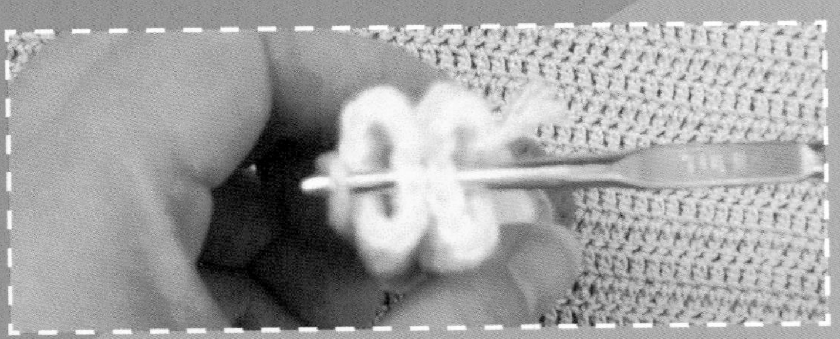

Diagram of how to connect legs together.

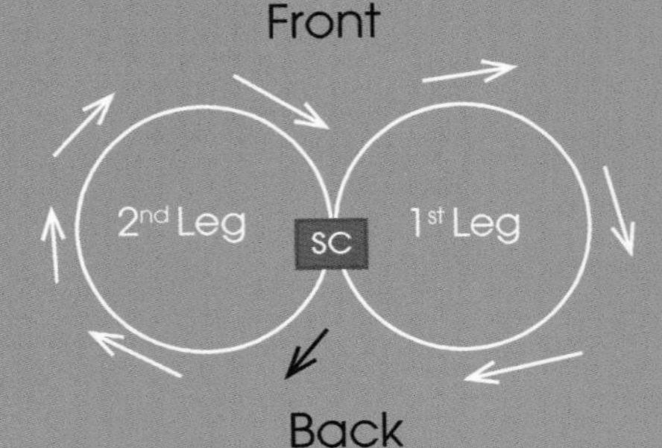

The sc is for connecting legs together and go through both legs. The next sc only go through second leg then go round.

Rnd 2: (Sc in next 4 sts, 2 sc in next st) around. (24)
Rnd 3: (Sc in next 3 sts, 2 sc in next st) around. (30)
Rnd 4: Sc in each st around.
Rnd 5: Sc in each st around, changing to **Red** in last 2 loops of last st.
Rnd 6: Sc in each st around.
Rnd 7: Working in back loops only. Sc in each st around.
Rnd 8: (Sc in next 3 sts, sc next 2 sts tog) around. (24)
Rnd 9: (Sc in next 4 sts, sc next 2 sts tog) around. (20)
Rnd 10: Sc in each st around.
Rnd 11: (Sc in next 4 sts, 2 sc in next st) around. (24)
Rnd 12-14: Sc in each st around.
Rnd 15: (Sc in next 2 sts, sc next 2 sts tog) around. (18)
Rnd 16: (Sc in next st, sc next 2 sts tog) around, changing to **Cream** in last 2 loops of last st. (12)
Rnd 17: Working in back loops only. (Sc in next st, 2 sc in next st) around. Stuff. (18)
Rnd 18: (2 sc in next st, sc in next 2 sts) around. (24)
Rnd 19: (Sc in next 3 sts, 2 sc in next st) around. (30)
Rnd 20: (Sc in next 4 sts, 2 sc in next st) around. (36)
Rnd 21: (Sc in next 5 sts, 2 sc in next st) around. (42)
Rnd 22: (Sc in next 6 sts, 2 sc in next st) around. (48)
Rnd 23: (Sc in next 7 sts, 2 sc in next st) around. (54)
Rnd 24-31: Sc in each st around.
Rnd 32: (Sc next 2 sts tog, sc in next 7 sts) around. (48)
Rnd 33: (Sc in next 6 sts, sc next 2 sts tog) around. (42)
Rnd 34: Sc in next 3 sts, sc next 2 sts tog, (sc in next 5 sts, sc next 2 sts tog) 5 times, sc in next 2 sts. (36)
Rnd 35: (Sc next 2 sts tog, sc in next 4 sts) around. (30)
Rnd 36: (Sc in next 3 sts, sc next 2 sts tog) around. (24)
Rnd 37: (Sc next 2 sts tog, sc in next 2 sts) around. Stuff. (18)
Rnd 38: (Sc in next st, sc next 2 sts tog) around. (12)
Rnd 39: (Sc next 2 sts tog) around, join with sl st in first st. Fasten off. (6)

Skirt

Rnd 1: Join **Red** to free loop of rnd 6, ch 1, sc in same st, sc in each st around. (30)
Rnd 2-3: Sc in each st around.
Rnd 4: (Sc in next 4 sts, 2 sc in next st) around. (36)
Rnd 5: (Sc in next 5 sts, 2 sc in next st) around. (42)
Rnd 6-7: Sc in each st around.
Rnd 8: Sc in each st around, changing to **Green** in last 2 loops of last st.
Rnd 9: Sc in each st around, join with sl st in first st. Fasten off.

Arm

Make 2.
Rnd 1: With **Red**, ch 2, 6 sc in second chain from hook. (6)
Rnd 2: (Sc in next st, 2 sc in next st) around. (9)
Rnd 3-7: Sc in each st around. (9)
Rnd 8: Sc in each st around, changing to **Green** in last 2 loops of last st. Stuff. (9)
Rnd 9: Sc in each st around, changing to **Cream** in last 2 loops of last st. Stuff. (9)
Rnd 10: Working in back loops only. (Sc in next st, sc next 2 sts tog) 3 times. (6)
Rnd 11: For thumb, 2 sc in first st, skip next 4 sts, 2 sc in next st, join with sl st in first st. Fasten off.

Rnd 11: For hand, join **Cream** to next free st on rnd 10, ch 1, 2 sc in same st, (2 sc in next st) 3 times. (8)
Rnd 12: Sc in each st around.
Row 13: Working in rows, flatten last rnd, matching sts and working through both thicknesses, sc in next 2 sts, sl st in next st. Fasten off.

Row 13					cxx	
Rnd 12		xx	xx	xx	xx	
Rnd 11	v	v	v	v	v	v
Rnd 10	x	x	x	x	x	x

White = hand
Black = thumb

x = sc
v = 2 sc in same st
c = slip stitch

Sew arms to body on rnds 13-14 with thumb towards front.

Belt

With **Green**, ch 31, sl st in second chain from hook, sl st in each ch across, fasten off. (30)

Sew belt over rnd 7 of body. With **Red**, using straight stitches, embroider buckle over belt.

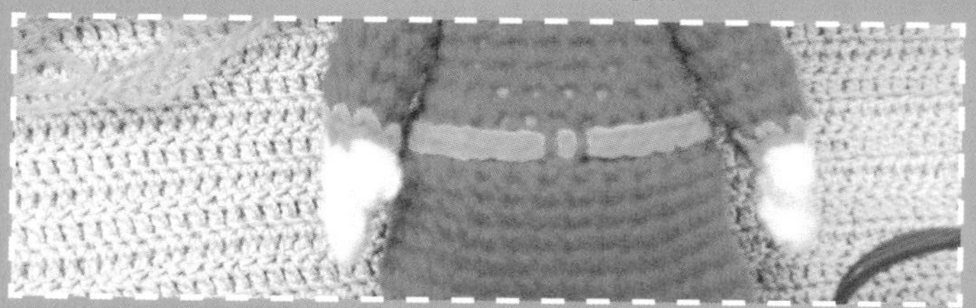

Hat

Rnd 1: With **Red**, ch 2, 6 sc in second chain from hook. (6)
Rnd 2: Sc in each st around.
Rnd 3: (Sc in next st, 2 sc in next st) around. (9)
Rnd 4: Sc in each st around.
Rnd 5: (2 sc in next st, sc in next 2 sts) around. (12)
Rnd 6-7: Sc in each st around.
Rnd 8: (2 sc in next st, sc in next 3 sts) around. (15)
Rnd 9: (Sc in next 4 sts, 2 sc in next st) around. (18)
Rnd 10: Sc in each st around.
Rnd 11: (Sc in next 5 sts, 2 sc in next st) around.(21)
Rnd 12: (Sc in next 6 sts, 2 sc in next st) around. (24)
Rnd 13: Sc in each st around.
Rnd 14: (2 sc in next st,sc in next 7 sts) around. (27)
Rnd 15: (Sc in next 8 sts, 2 sc in next st) around. (30)
Rnd 16: Sc in each st around.
Rnd 17: (Sc in next 9 sts, 2 sc in next st) around. (33)
Rnd 18: (Sc in next 10 sts, 2 sc in next st) around. (36)
Rnd 19: Sc in each st around.
Rnd 20: (Sc in next 11 sts, 2 sc in next st) around.(39)
Rnd 21: (Sc in next 12 sts, 2 sc in next st) around. (42)
Rnd 22: (2 sc in next st,sc in next 13 sts) around. (45)
Rnd 23: (Sc in next 14 sts, 2 sc in next st) around. (48)
Rnd 24: (Sc in next 7 sts, 2 sc in next st) around. (54)
Rnd 25: (Sc in next 8 sts, 2 sc in next st) around. (60)
Rnd 26-29: Sc in each st around.
Rnd 30: Sc in each st around, changing to **Green** in last 2 loops of last st.

Rnd 31: Working in front loops only. Sc in each st around.
Rnd 32: Sc in each st around, join with sl st in first st, fasten off.

Sew a small bell on top of hat.

Hair

With **Peach**, wind the yarn loosely and evenly around a 5.5 inch (14 cm) piece of card board until the card is filled, then cut across one edge, repeat as needed. For fringe, hold 1 strand of yarn, fold in half. With wrong side of hat facing, insert hook in free loop of rnd 30, draw the folded end through the stitch and pull the loose ends through the folded end, draw the knot up tightly. Add fringe around. Sew hat on head. For hair you can do the pigtails or braids as you wish. I did 2 braids.

Finishing

Sew eyes 8 sts apart over rnds 25-26 of head. With **Red**, embroider mouth.

Santa, Snowman and Christmas Tree

EASY

Size

Santa and Snowman are 5 inches/ 13 cm tall (excluding hat).
The christmas tree is 6 inches/ 15 cm tall (excluding star).

Materials

- Sport, 4 ply yarn
  Clolors: White, Red, Green, Light Green, Yellow and Black
- 3.00 mm and 4.00 mm hooks
- Polyester fiberfill
- Black bead 4 mm for eyes or use other eyes as desired
- Tapestry needle
- Sewing needle and thread for attaching eyes

Remarks

This project is working in continuous rounds, do not join or turn unless otherwise stated. Mark first stitch of each round.

You can use DK yarn  instead of Sport/ 4 ply yarn.

Use 4.00 mm hook instead of 3.00 mm hook and use 5.00 mm hooks instead of 4.00 mm hook.

Santa

Head and Body

Rnd 1: Starting at the bottom of the body. With **Red**, ch 2, 6 sc in second chain from hook. (6)
Rnd 2: 2 sc in each st around. (12)
Rnd 3: (Sc in next st, 2 sc in next st) around. (18)
Rnd 4: (2 sc in next st, sc in next 2 sts) around. (24)
Rnd 5: Sc in next 2 sts, 2 sc in next st, (sc in next 3 sts, 2 sc in next st) 5 times, sc in next st. (30)
Rnd 6: (Sc in next 4 sts,2 sc in next st) around.(36)
Rnd 7: (2 sc in next st, sc in next 5 sts) around. (42)
Rnd 8: Sc in next 3 sts, 2 sc in next st, (sc in next 6 sts, 2 sc in next st) 5 times, sc in next 3 sts. (48)
Rnd 9: (Sc in next 7 sts, 2 sc in next st) around. (54)
Rnd 10: Sc in next 4 sts, 2 sc in next st, (sc in next 8 sts, 2 sc in next st) 5 times, sc in next 4 sts. (60)
Rnd 11: Working in back loops only. Sc in each st around.
Rnd 12: Sc in each st around.
Rnd 13: Working in back loops only. Sc in each st around.
Rnd 14-20: Sc in each st around.
Rnd 21: (Sc in next 8 sts, sc next 2sts tog) around. (54)
Rnd 22: Sc in each st around.
Rnd 23: (Sc in next 7 sts, sc next 2 sts tog) around. (48)
Rnd 24: Sc in each st around.
Rnd 25: Sc in next 3 sts, sc next 2 sts tog, (sc in next 6 sts, sc next 2 sts tog) 5 times, sc in next 3 sts. (42)
Rnd 26: Sc in each st around.
Rnd 27: (Sc in next 5 sts, sc next 2 sts tog) around. (36)
Rnd 28: Sc in each st around. Stuff.
Rnd 29: Sc in next 2 sts, sc next 2 sts tog, (sc in next 4 sts, sc next 2 sts tog) 5 times, sc in next 2 sts. (30)
Rnd 30: (Sc next 2 sts tog, sc in next 3 sts) around, changing to **Cream** in last 2 loops of last st. (24)
Rnd 31-36: Sc in each st around.
Rnd 37: (Sc in next 2 sts, sc next 2 sts tog) around. Stuff. (18)
Rnd 38: (Sc in next st, sc next 2 sts tog) around. (12)
Rnd 39: (Sc next 2 sts tog) around, join with sl st in first st. Fasten off.

Edge of Shirt

Rnd 1: Join **White** to free loop of rnd 12 , ch 1, sc in same st, sc in each st around. (60)

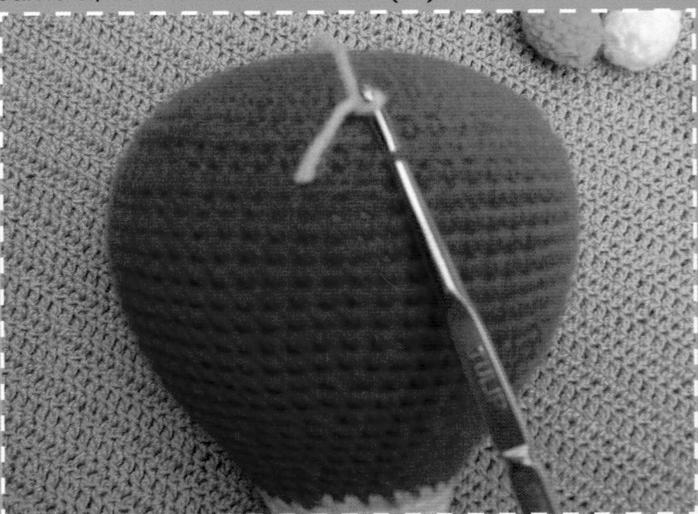

Rnd 2: Sl st in next st, ch 1, reverse sc in each st around, join with sl st in first st. Fasten off.

Note: Reverse sc is working from left to right, insert hook in next st to the right and complete as sc.

Hat

Rnd 1: With **Red**, ch 2, 6 sc in second chain from hook. (6)
Rnd 2-3: Sc in each st around.
Rnd 4: (Sc in next st, 2 sc in next st) around. (9)
Rnd 5-6: Sc in each st around.
Rnd 7: (2 sc in next st, sc in next 2 sts) around. (12)
Rnd 8-9: Sc in each st around.
Rnd 10: (2 sc in next st, sc in next 3 sts) around.(15)
Rnd 11-12: Sc in each st around.
Rnd 13: (Sc in next 4 sts, 2 sc in next st) around. (18)
Rnd 14-15: Sc in each st around.
Rnd 16: (Sc in next 5 sts, 2 sc in next st) around.(21)
Rnd 17-18: Sc in each st around.
Rnd 19: (Sc in next 6 sts, 2 sc in next st) around. (24)
Rnd 20-21: Sc in each st around.
Rnd 22: (Sc in next 7 sts, 2 sc in next st) around. (27)
Rnd 23: Sc in each st around, changing to **White** in last 2 loops of last st.
Rnd 24: Sc in each st around.
Rnd 25: Sl st in ext st, ch 1, reverse sc in each st around, join with sl st in first st. Fasten off.

Pom-pom: Wrap **White** around small cardboard 10 times, slide loops off cardboard; tie separate strand around middle of all loops. Cut loops, trim and sew to top of hat.

Arm

Make 2.

Rnd 1: With **Red**, ch 2, 6 sc in second chain from hook. (6)
Rnd 2-7: Sc in each st around.
Rnd 8: Sc in each st around, changing to **White** in last 2 loops of last st.
Rnd 9: 2 sc in each st around, changing to **Light Green** in last 2 loops of last st. (12)
Rnd 10-12: Sc in each st around. Stuff.
Rnd 13: Sc next 2 sts tog around, join with sl st in first st, fasten off. Sew opening closed. (6)

Only stuff hands. Sew arms to side of body over rnd 23-24.

Belt

With **Black**, ch 61, sc in second chain from hook, sc in each chain across. Leave long end for sewing, fasten off.

Sew belt over rnds 17-18 of the body.
With **Yellow**, using straight stitches, embroider buckle over belt.

Beard

Part 1 Working in rows.
Row 1: With **White**, ch 25, sc in second chain from hook, sc in each st across, turn. (24)
Row 2: Ch 1, lp st in each st across. Leave long end for sewing, fasten off. (24)

> **Loop stitch** (lp st): warp yarn clockwise around one finger one time, insert hook in next stitch and through loop on finger, draw loop through stitch, yarn over, draw through 2 loops on hook.

Part 2 Working in rows.
Row 1: With **White**, ch 2, 2 sc in second chain from hook, turn. (2)
Row 2: Ch 1, lp st in each st across, turn. (2)
Row 3: Ch 1, 2 sc in each st across, turn. (4)
Row 4: Ch 1, lp st in each st across, turn. (4)
Row 5: Ch 1, 2 sc in first st, sc in next 2 sts, 2 sc in last st, turn. (6)
Row 6: Ch 1, lp st in each st across, turn. (6)
Row 7: Ch 1, 2 sc in first st, sc in next 4 sts, 2 sc in last st, turn. (8)
Row 8: Ch 1, lp st in each st across. Leave long end for sewing, fasten off. (8)

Sew row 8 of Part 2 in the middle of Part 1 on row 1.

Pin beard on rnds 32-33 of head and sew.

Mustache

With **White**, ch 6, sl st in second chain from hook, sc in next ch, sl st in next ch, sc in next ch, sl st in next ch, fasten off.

Finishing Santa

Sew hat on head.
Sew eyes 4 sts apart over rnds 36-37 of head.
With **Red**, embroider mouth.
Sew mustache above mouth.

Snowman

Head and Body

Rnd 1: Starting at the bottom of the body. With **White**, ch 2, 6 sc in second chain from hook. (6)
Rnd 2: 2 sc in each st around. (12)
Rnd 3: (Sc in next st, 2 sc in next st) around. (18)
Rnd 4: (2 sc in next st, sc in next 2 sts) around. (24)
Rnd 5: Sc in next 2 sts, 2 sc in next st, (sc in next 3 sts, 2 sc in next st) 5 times, sc in next st. (30)
Rnd 6: (Sc in next 4 sts,2 sc in next st) around.(36)
Rnd 7: (2 sc in next st, sc in next 5 sts) around. (42)
Rnd 8: Sc in next 3 sts, 2 sc in next st, (sc in next 6 sts, 2 sc in next st) 5 times, sc in next 3 sts. (48)
Rnd 9: (Sc in next 7 sts, 2 sc in next st) around. (54)
Rnd 10: Sc in next 4 sts, 2 sc in next st, (sc in next 8 sts, 2 sc in next st) 5 times, sc in next 4 sts. (60)
Rnd 11: Working in back loops only. Sc in each st around.
Rnd 12-20: Sc in each st around.
Rnd 21: (Sc in next 8 sts, sc next 2sts tog) around. (54)
Rnd 22: Sc in each st around.
Rnd 23: (Sc in next 7 sts, sc next 2 sts tog) around. (48)
Rnd 24: Sc in each st around.
Rnd 25: Sc in next 3 sts, sc next 2 sts tog, (sc in next 6 sts, sc next 2 sts tog) 5 times, sc in next 3 sts. (42)
Rnd 26: Sc in each st around.
Rnd 27: (Sc in next 5 sts, sc next 2 sts tog) around. (36)
Rnd 28: Sc in each st around. Stuff.
Rnd 29: Sc in next 2 sts, sc next 2 sts tog, (sc in next 4 sts, sc next 2 sts tog) 5 times, sc in next 2 sts. (30)
Rnd 30: (Sc next 2 sts tog, sc in next 3 sts) around. (24)
Rnd 31-36: Sc in each st around.
Rnd 37: (Sc in next 2 sts, sc next 2 sts tog) around. Stuff. (18)
Rnd 38: (Sc in next st, sc next 2 sts tog) around. (12)
Rnd 39: (Sc next 2 sts tog) around, join with sl st in first st. Fasten off.

Arm of Snowman

Make 2.
Rnd 1: With **White**, ch 2, 6 sc in second chain from hook. (6)
Rnd 2-8: Sc in each st around.
Rnd 9: 2 sc in each st around. (12)
Rnd 10-12: Sc in each st around. Stuff.
Rnd 13: Sc next 2 sts tog around, join with sl st in first st. Fasten off. Sew opening closed. (6)

Only stuff hand. Sew arms to side of body over rnds 23-24.

Scarf

With one strand of **Red** and **Green** and 4 mm hook; Ch 60, sc in second chain from hook, sc in each ch across, fasten off. Put scarf on snowman.

Snowman Hat

Rnd 1: With **Black**, ch 2, 6 sc in second chain from hook. (6)
Rnd 2: 2 sc in each st around. (12)
Rnd 3: Working in back loops only. Sc in each st around.
Rnd 4-5: Sc in each st around.
Rnd 6: (Sc in next st, 2 sc in next st) around. (18)
Rnd 7: Sc in each st around, join with sl st in first st. Fasten off.

Tie a bow on hat with **Red** and **Green** yarns.

Finishing Snowman

Sew eyes 5 sts apart over rnds 36-37 of head.
With **Black**, embroider mouth. Stuff hat and sew on head.

Christmas Tree

Rnd 1: With **Green**, ch 2, 6 sc in second chain from hook. (6)
Rnd 2: 2 sc in each st around. (12)
Rnd 3: (Sc in next st, 2 sc in next st) around. (18)
Rnd 4: (Sc in next 2 sts, 2 sc in next st) around. (24)
Rnd 5: (Sc in next 3 sts, 2 sc in next st) around. (30)
Rnd 6: (Sc in next 4 sts,2 sc in next st) around.(36)
Rnd 7: (Sc in next 5 sts, 2 sc in next st) around. (42)
Rnd 8: (Sc in next 6 sts, 2 sc in next st) around. (48)
Rnd 9: (Sc in next 7 sts, 2 sc in next st) around. (54)
Rnd 10: (Sc in next 8 sts, 2 sc in next st) around. (60)
Rnd 11: Working in back loops only. Sc in each st around.
Rnd 12-13: Sc in each st around.
Rnd 14: Working in back loops only. Sc in each st around.
Rnd 15-16: Sc in each st around.
Rnd 17: Working in back loops only. Sc in each st around.
Rnd 18-19: Sc in each st around.
Rnd 20: Working in back loops only. (Sc in next 8 sts, sc next 2sts tog) around. (54)
Rnd 21-22: Sc in each st around.
Rnd 23: Working in back loops only. (Sc in next 7 sts, sc next 2 sts tog) around. (48)
Rnd 24-25: Sc in each st around.
Rnd 26: Working in back loops only. (Sc in next 6 sts, sc next 2 sts tog) around. (42)
Rnd 27-28: Sc in each st around.
Rnd 29: Working in back loops only. (Sc in next 5 sts, sc next 2 sts tog) around. (36)
Rnd 30-31: Sc in each st around. Stuff.
Rnd 32: Working in back loops only. (Sc in next 4 sts, sc next 2 sts tog) around. (30)
Rnd 33-34: Sc in each st around.
Rnd 35: Working in back loops only. (Sc in next 3 sts, sc next 2 sts tog) around. (24)
Rnd 36-37: Sc in each st around.
Rnd 38: Working in back loops only. (Sc in next 2 sts, sc next 2 sts tog) around. Stuff. (18)
Rnd 39-40: Sc in each st around.
Rnd 41: Working in back loops only. (Sc in next st, sc next 2 sts tog) around. (12)
Rnd 42-43: Sc in each st around. Stuff.
Rnd 44: Working in back loops only. (Sc next 2 sts tog) around, join with sl st in first st. Fasten off

Needles or Fringe

Row 1: Join **Green** to free loop of rnd 13, ch 1, sc in same st, ch 6, sl st in third chain from hook, ch 3, sc in next st, (sc in next st, ch 6, sl st in third chain from hook, ch 3, sc in next st) 29 times. Fasten off.

Row 2: Join **Green** to free loop of rnd 16, ch 1, sc in same st, ch 6, sl st in third chain from hook, ch 3, sc in next st, (sc in next st, ch 6, sl st in third chain from hook, ch 3, sc in next st) 29 times. Fasten off.

Row 3: Join **Green** to free loop of rnd 19, ch 1, sc in same st, ch 6, sl st in third chain from hook, ch 3, sc in next st, (sc in next st, ch 6, sl st in third chain from hook, ch 3, sc in next st) 29 times. Fasten off.
Row 4: Join **Green** to free loop of rnd 22, ch 1, sc in same st, ch 6, sl st in third chain from hook, ch 3, sc in next st, (sc in next st, ch 6, sl st in third chain from hook, ch 3, sc in next st) 26 times. Fasten off.
Row 5: Join **Green** to free loop of rnd 25, ch 1, sc in same st, ch 6, sl st in third chain from hook, ch 3, sc in next st, (sc in next st, ch 6, sl st in third chain from hook, ch 3, sc in next st) 23 times. Fasten off.
Row 6: Join **Green** to free loop of rnd 28, ch 1, sc in same st, ch 6, sl st in third chain from hook, ch 3, sc in next st, (sc in next st, ch 6, sl st in third chain from hook, ch 3, sc in next st) 20 times. Fasten off.
Row 7: Join **Green** to free loop of rnd 31, ch 1, sc in same st, ch 6, sl st in third chain from hook, ch 3, sc in next st, (sc in next st, ch 6, sl st in third chain from hook, ch 3, sc in next st) 17 times. Fasten off.
Row 8: Join **Green** to free loop of rnd 34, ch 1, sc in same st, ch 6, sl st in third chain from hook, ch 3, sc in next st, (sc in next st, ch 6, sl st in third chain from hook, ch 3, sc in next st) 14 times. Fasten off.
Row 9: Join **Green** to free loop of rnd 37, ch 1, sc in same st, ch 6, sl st in third chain from hook, ch 3, sc in next st, (sc in next st, ch 6, sl st in third chain from hook, ch 3, sc in next st) 11 times. Fasten off.
Row 10: Join **Green** to free loop of rnd 40, ch 1, sc in same st, ch 6, sl st in third chain from hook, ch 3, sc in next st, (sc in next st, ch 6, sl st in third chain from hook, ch 3, sc in next st) 8 times. Fasten off.
Row 11: Join **Green** to free loop of rnd 43, ch 1, sc in same st, ch 6, sl st in third chain from hook, ch 3, sc in next st, (sc in next st, ch 6, sl st in third chain from hook, ch 3, sc in next st) 5 times. Fasten off.

Star

Make 2.
Rnd 1: With **Yellow**, ch 2, 5 sc in second chain from hook. (5)
Rnd 2: (Ch 4, sl st in third chain from hook, ch 1, sl st in next st) 5 times. Leave long end for sewing, fasten off.

Matching sts, hold 2 pieces of stars together and sew them. Sew star on top of tree.

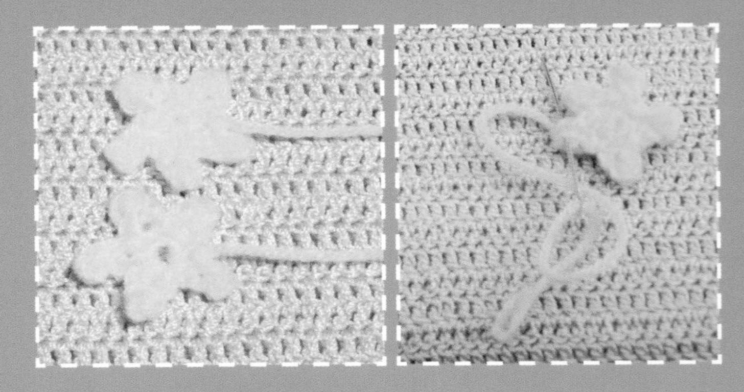

Garland

Whit **Red**, ch 2, (6 sc in second chain from hook, ch 10) 20 times, fasten off.

With **White**, ch 2, (6 sc in second chain from hook, ch 10) 20 times, fasten off. Twisted them together and put around the tree.

How to join Yarn.

Join yarn to free loop, ch 1, sc in same st.

How to embroider mouth.

How to read pattern.

Rnd 4: (Sc in next 2 sts, 2 sc in next st) around. (24)

Number (24) at the end of round = number of stitches after finished round.

Rnd 5: (Sc in next 3 sts, 2 sc in next st) around. (30)

Repeat (Sc in next 3 sts, 2 sc in next st) until end of round

=> **Rnd 5:** (Sc in next 3 sts, 2 sc in next st), (Sc in next 3 sts, 2 sc in next st), (Sc in next 3 sts, 2 sc in next st), (Sc in next 3 sts, 2 sc in next st), (Sc in next 3 sts, 2 sc in next st), (Sc in next 3 sts, 2 sc in next st)

Total stitches of Rnd 5 = 5+5+5+5+5+5 = 30 sts

Rnd 6: Sc in next 2 sts, 2 sc in next st, (sc in next 4 sts, 2 sc in next st) 5 times, sc in next 2 sts. (36)

Repeat (sc in next 4 sts, 2 sc in next st) 5 times

=> **Rnd 6:** Sc in next 2 sts, 2 sc in next st, (sc in next 4 sts, 2 sc in next st), (sc in next 4 sts, 2 sc in next st), (sc in next 4 sts, 2 sc in next st), (sc in next 4 sts, 2 sc in next st), (sc in next 4 sts, 2 sc in next st), sc in next 2 sts.

Total stitches of Rnd 6 = 2+2+6+6+6+6+6+2 = 36 sts

Huggy Dolls Amigurumi
Subtitle: 15 Huggable Doll Patterns
Publisher: K and J Publishing
Author: Sayjai Thawornsupacharoen
Publication date: 14th of June 2014
ISBN: 978-1910407028

Easy Amigurumi
Subtitle: 28 doll patterns
Publisher: K and J Publishing
Author: Sayjai Thawornsupacharoen
Publication date: 18th of July 2014
ISBN: 978-1910407011

Dress Up Dolls Amigurumi
Subtitle: 5 big dolls with clothes, shoes, accessories, tiny bear and big carry bag patterns
Publisher: K and J Publishing
Author: Sayjai Thawornsupacharoen
Publication date:
27th of September 2014
ISBN: 978-1910407066

Sunny Amigurumi
Subtitle: Crochet Patterns
Publisher: K and J Publishing
Author: Sayjai Thawornsupacharoen
Editor: Robert Appelboom
Date of publication:
25th of February 2015
ISBN: 978-1910407189

Copyright

Copyright © 2015 Sayjai Thawornsupacharoen. All rights reserved. Cannot be reproduced or published online without the explicit permission of Sayjai Thawornsupacharoen.
For information on licensing please send an e-mail to: kandjdolls@gmail.com.

You can sell finished dolls based on these patterns provided they are handmade.
You have to make and sell them yourself in a craft store or market. You can only sell a limited small number (only a handful). It is a requirement to add the following note to your online advertisement and to the doll itself:
The design for this doll is from Sayjai Thawornsupacharoen, © 2015 Sayjai, All rights reserved.

This book is for your personal use only. Please respect Sayjai's copyright and do not share this book online.

First Edition
Date of publication: 19th of November 2015
Editor: Robert Appelboom
Publisher: K and J Publishing
Cambridge, England

http://kandjdolls.blogspot.co.uk
www.facebook.com/kandjdolls.amigurumi.patterns

Printed in Great Britain
by Amazon